boilerplate CW01024392

Adult ADHD Solution

The Complete Guide to Understanding and
Managing Adult ADHD to Overcome
Impulsivity, Hyperactivity, Inattention,
Stress, and Anxiety

MR. ASHIYA & BRANDON ANSTIN M.D.

Table of Contents

Introduction

Most adults are familiar with these two terms: attention deficit disorder (ADD) and attention deficit/hyperactivity disorder (ADHD). The term "ADD" is outdated and has been dropped as a diagnostic term. ADHD is the official medical term for the condition regardless of whether a person shows symptoms of hyperactivity. "ADD" is still used in casual speech to refer to Inattentive type ADHD. From a medical literature standpoint, there are three types of ADHD:

Type 1: Inattentive ADHD

When someone uses the term "ADD" they are usually referring to Inattentive ADHD. This type occurs when a person shows symptoms of inattention but isn't hyperactive/impulsive.

Type 2: Hyperactive-Impulsive ADHD

This means a person has symptoms of hyperactivity and impulsivity but not inattention.

Type 3: Combination ADHD

This occurs when a person has symptoms of inattention, hyperactivity, and impulsivity.

What a lot of people don't know is that ADHD is actually very common in adults too. Initially, ADHD was considered condition that could be grown out of. However, in more recent years, the medical field has begun to recognize it as condition that is lifelong and can impact people throughout their entire lives.

Perhaps you have just received a diagnosis of adult ADHD. Maybe you were told you had it as a child, but always assumed that you grew out of it. You may have known you have it for a while, but have been struggling to manage the day-to-day challenges that adult ADHD presents. Whatever your reasons for seeking out *Adult ADHD Solution,* you won't be disappointed!

Adult ADHD Solution has been written as a guide for adults with ADHD to help them organize their lives and learn how to manage this condition. It is also meant to help you overcome the most severe symptoms that accompany adult ADHD, symptoms that can interfere with day-to-day life, relationships, families, and jobs.

ADHD is classified as a mental health condition that has roots in neurological imbalances. It leads to low self-esteem, poor ethics and skills, and reduced performance in work, as well as unstable relationships.

Generally, as children grow into adults, the hyperactivity component of ADHD mellows out. This doesn't mean that hyperactivity doesn't manifest in other ways though.

Usually, neurological disorders are a result of a mix-up in the brain. They can be the result of "crossed wires" which leads the wrong signals to the wrong parts of the body. They can be the result of environmental factors that the body and mind have been exposed to, creating that imbalance in the brain. Some neurological disorders are genetic.

Most children and adults who are diagnosed with ADHD end up on prescription medications long term, if not for their whole lives. One of the greatest takeaways that you will get from this book is different holistic and self-care tips on how to manage and treat your adult ADHD without relying on medication. With a lifelong condition, long-term medication has its risks. If you've been on medication for a long time or don't want to use pharmaceuticals to treat your ADHD, then you can learn a lot from *Adult ADHD Solution*.

As an adult with ADHD, you are likely familiar with these symptoms and the struggles you face. If you were only recently diagnosed, however, you might learn about struggles you always faced and never knew what they were related to. For example, forming patterns and sticking to a schedule can be a very hard task for adults with ADHD, leading to common bouts of depression. A doctor might easily diagnose depression, but not know that the cause is actually related to ADHD.

Have you been looking for a way to lead a more fulfilling, productive life? Have you been curious to learn how to overcome the struggles that come with adult ADHD? In the course of reading *Adult ADHD Solution*, you'll learn more about these residual symptoms. You will also learn some of the most effective ways people with similar brain patterns and neurology to you have been able to manage these symptoms.

Mental health conditions can be scary. There is still a great stigma around mental health. Even with all the psychology and medical progress and research, mental health is not looked on with kindness. It is incredibly sad and unfortunate because most adults do struggle with a mental health condition at some point in their life. Don't be afraid of an adult ADHD diagnosis. Even though it isn't as talked about as it should be, there is plenty of information to help lead you towards a happier, healthier, more fulfilling life.

A diagnosis of a mental health condition like ADHD should be taken seriously. Don't think we are suggesting that you shouldn't, just because the majority of society holds stigmas around it. You just need to find the best tools and skills to handle your own mental health. The best tool to help you in combating the struggles and symptoms of ADHD is education. By educating yourself on ADHD, you will most likely learn a lot more about yourself and answer a lot of your own questions about why certain aspects of your life always seem to be falling apart or not working.

You can learn how to manage your ADHD, and we can help you on that road with some of the best, most recent, and top-notch scientific information. You will also have access to information, tips, and tricks from adults who have battled ADHD to find their own success. Hopefully you will find inspiration through this wisdom to improve your own circumstances. While everyone is different, oftentimes people with the same neurological disorders can find success and relief in the same approaches.

Please keep in mind that this book is not a diagnostic manual. The information on ADHD isn't a substitute for a professional health care diagnosis or a treatment plan from a qualified healthcare provider.

So, if this is all new territory for you, or if you are looking to make a major change, we think you've made an excellent decision to educate yourself and learn from those who have already overcome their struggles and have decided to pass on their knowledge to others in similar situations. This is your starting point to take control of your own life, future, and success. It's time to learn about your mind and start working with it instead of against it.

Chapter 1:
Adult ADHD

When it comes to childhood behavior, the term ADHD has become more and more common to describe children that have too much energy, can't focus, or don't listen to their parents for one reason or another. It is quite commonplace for adults to have children, or know other parents with children, that have received a diagnosis of ADHD. You probably know someone who had ADHD growing up, or know a parent that has a child that has been diagnosed.

As far as adults with ADHD, the truth behind the statistics is still being collected and evaluated. In recent years, it has been suggested that adult ADHD is actually a lot more common than previously thought. Roughly 4.4% of adults in the US have adult ADHD. It might seem like a small percent, but in regard to neurological disorders, it is rather high with more than 33 million new adult cases being diagnosed a year. It is more common for adult men to have adult ADHD with 5.4% of adult males having it and 3.2% of adult females having adult ADHD. (ADHD Editorial Board, 2020).

Adult ADHD has only been accepted as a recognized condition in more recent years. Initially, it was thought that children with ADHD would grow out of their symptoms, calming down as they matured. Since it was realized that ADHD is a neurological condition and not a behavior condition, it is now considered a lifelong condition. If you're an adult struggling with ADHD symptoms now, then there is a chance it is a re-diagnosis from your youth. Now, it is possible that you were never recognized as having ADHD as a child. Getting a new diagnosis in adulthood, especially for a condition that has long been considered a childhood disorder, can be disorienting.

This chapter is going to cover what adult ADHD is, how it differs from the childhood version, signs and symptoms, risk factors, and also some myths and facts. This will better help you understand what it is that you have and why it impacts your life in certain ways. Fortunately, ADHD is a neurological condition that can be easily managed with medication, and just as effectively managed through your lifestyle.

ADHD in Adulthood

In the last decade, cases of diagnosed adult ADHD have risen significantly. Anywhere from 6% to 30% of children that are diagnosed with ADHD carry it into adulthood, although that percentage is probably higher than estimated. Not all of the adult ADHD diagnoses are carrying over from childhood either. This means they are new cases coming up for adults.

Most scientific professionals do think that ADHD is grossly underdiagnosed in adults in the US. (ADHD Editorial Staff, 2020).

So, what does ADHD look like in adults?

The symptoms that are associated with adult ADHD can severely impact an individual's ability to get and maintain a job. It can also lead to an individual's inability to rise in rank and position in the workplace. This is especially true for those that never got ADHD treatment in childhood.

If you're pursuing higher or additional education opportunities, ADHD can cause problems with doing schoolwork, especially when it comes to time management. Maybe you've always had trouble in school, no matter how hard you tried, and never knew why. ADHD could very well be the answer to that question.

As far as relationships go, adults with ADHD can struggle with interpersonal relationships. This includes family relationships, friendships, romantic relationships, coworkers, and other social interactions. It can be incredibly disheartening to have constant complications in relationships. Most people do have a desire for companionship and romance in their lives. Without knowing it, prior to an ADHD diagnosis, the symptoms could have been contributing to problems and difficulty sustaining romantic partnership.

Understanding these differences in how an ADHD mind and personality work versus a neurotypical person (someone without a neurological disorder) is going to give you an advantage towards success. You might even be able to salvage some rocky relationships by offering explanations and committing to managing your symptoms.

It is an unfortunate reality, but adults with ADHD do tend to end up with legal complications and in potentially harmful situations. This is often a byproduct of impulsivity as a symptom of ADHD. It can also stem from trouble keeping a job and advancing through school. Sometimes criminal behavior becomes easier than trying to struggle through the more difficult tasks.

In fact, children who present ADHD symptoms are more likely to engage in criminal activity as adults than children who don't. There is also statistical information to show that adults with ADHD are more likely to get into car crashes than those who don't. Now, that doesn't mean every adult who has been in a car accident has adult ADHD, or that because you've never been in a car accident, you've been misdiagnosed.

There are plenty of adults with ADHD who are not criminally inclined and who don't find themselves in dangerous situations. If you are one of those adults, fantastic! You're already heading in the right direction towards managing your symptoms. Without knowing it, you've probably picked up a few tips for self-management without even knowing it.

Another commonality with adults with ADHD is that they are two times as likely to have substance use disorder (SUD) than neurotypical adults. More often than not, adults with ADHD and SUD have reported that they resort to substances like alcohol and marijuana to manage their symptoms. Sometimes even stronger substances are used for self-medication. Marijuana has been known to help with the hyperactivity in adult ADHD.

The field of medical marijuana is growing; however, it won't be included in the holistic treatment options section as it is still a mask for the symptoms, much like medication. The goal of holistic and self-treatment is to alter your lifestyle to manage your symptoms naturally and organically, not put a 'Band-Aid' on them with substances and medications.

One of the major associations with ADHD in adults, and very likely the reason your doctor ended up with this diagnosis, is comorbid conditions. What this means is that it is uncommon for ADHD to exist in adults without a second condition presenting itself as well. Often, these conditions are more prevalent and can be more detrimental, hiding the ADHD symptoms underneath.

Roughly 40% of adults with ADHD have also been diagnosed with a mood disorder. 19% alone have been diagnosed with depression. Mood disorders can also include manic depressive disorder and seasonal affective disorder. A lot of mood disorders have some extreme ups and downs and hard-to-manage symptoms. If you've been diagnosed with ADHD, then you might have also been treated for a mood disorder at some point in your life, or are currently being treated.

The most common comorbid conditions that include ADHD in adults are anxiety disorders. This includes general anxiety disorder (GAD), post-traumatic stress disorder and complex post-traumatic stress disorder (PTSD and CPTSD), and phobias. A phobia is an incredibly severe anxiety that can cause crippling panic attacks and irrational behavior for situations or potential situations. About 50% of adults with ADHD have been diagnosed with an anxiety disorder as well. Some of the ADHD symptoms do tie directly into anxiety, which will be elaborated on in a later section in this chapter.

SUD occurs in about 15% of adults with ADHD. It is possible that you aren't aware of any secondary condition or disorder. You could also be very fortunate to not have that additional hindrance. However, if you haven't been diagnosed with mood, anxiety, or substance use disorders, you might want to take a closer look at how you've been impacted by certain symptoms and events. You might be missing something.

Having adult ADHD can interfere with leading a 'normal' life, or rather the kind of life that you want for yourself. It isn't the end of the world, because by the end of this book, you'll have a lot of new information to help you achieve your goals.

Childhood ADHD

The three common symptoms that are used to diagnose ADHD in children are inattention, hyperactivity, and impulsivity. Children with ADHD often present with low self-esteem. This can usually be a result of pressures from family and friends who don't understand the symptoms that they are presenting.

With children, an earlier diagnosis is usually better as it can help deter some of the situations that adults find themselves in. Treatment and behavioral therapy in the younger years gives children skills to use as they advance into adolescence and adulthood.

Most childhood ADHD cases can be diagnosed before the age of seven in children. However, some do slip through the cracks or don't show up until teenage or adult years. In children, this particular neurodevelopmental condition can result in a child's inability to control their spontaneous responses. These responses may be physical, verbal, or emotional. They might blurt things out without thinking, impulsively lash out with their arms or legs, and explode with extreme emotions.

Children with ADHD are also known to struggle with their schoolwork. Prior to understanding this neurodevelopmental condition, a lot of children with these symptoms were considered 'troublemakers' and they were often punished for their behavior. It wasn't understood that these symptoms were beyond their control.

Fortunately, psychology has advanced to reveal that there are other ways to address these symptoms that give children ways to cope and manage themselves.

There is a common misconception with children that kids with ADHD are all hyperactive, can't focus, and don't pay attention. Truthfully, children who sit still for hours and "space out" are also prime candidates for ADHD, as are the kids who can't sit still or stop talking. There are a lot of extremes when it comes to the behavior and symptoms that present for ADHD. Separating symptoms from normal childhood behavior is even more confusing.

Depending on the age of the child or youth, there are also some key signs that can indicate ADHD over normal behavior. For example, preschoolers aren't known for their ability to focus and follow directions. However, a less common behavior is taking risky action, jumping off the top of the playground for instance, or blurting out insults without any filter or restraint.

Once a child hits school age, five or six, they should be able to sit still and pay attention. Therefore, hyperactivity, inattentiveness, and impulsivity symptoms stand out much more.

Like with any disorder, symptoms can range from mild and almost unnoticeable to severe. The more severe symptoms, when carried into adulthood, can cause a lot of harm in a person's professional life and personal life.

Normal Childhood Behaviour Vs. ADHD

During childhood development, there is a certain expectation for hyperactivity, inattention, and impulsivity. Children are still learning about themselves, their personalities, what their bodies are capable of, and how they fit in the world and society. Young children commonly have short attention spans, which is why most school programs don't start until around the age of five or six when a longer attention span has developed. Yet, even with children in their teen years, attention span can and often is directly linked to their interest level in the subject or activity.

Hyperactivity can be difficult to differentiate from natural childhood energy. Younger children often have a lot more energy. Most parents don't have the energy to keep up with their children all day every day, and this can make the children seem out of control, hyperactive even. Depending on genetics, personality, and physicality, some children just have more energy in general. Children having different energy levels than their friends or siblings is not a defining factor of ADHD. Hyperactivity is not the same as a "high energy level."

Some hyperactivity isn't even physical and doesn't manifest as movement and constant energy. Hyperactivity can be mental and result in a constantly active mind. Children with a mental hyperactivity might show a very intense creativity or imagination. They might have trouble sleeping because their mind won't rest, talk very fast and trip over their words in a rush to get their thoughts out, or just have a mind that moves at a million miles per hour with thoughts and ideas. This kind of hyperactivity might never be noticeable beyond verbal indications when conversing with that child.

If a child is struggling at school but is fine at home and with friends, they probably don't have ADHD. The same is true inversely for a child who struggles at home and with peers but excels at school. If a child has several of the ADHD symptoms that manifest in many different aspects of their life, and don't go away as they grow and develop, then there is a good chance they have ADHD.

As a neurological disorder, the symptoms won't come and go or ebb and flow. They'll be consistent. Childhood development and behavior can result in 'phases' and different developmental behaviors and traits that look like ADHD but aren't consistent.

Myths and Facts About ADHD

As with any mental health condition and neurological disorder where behavior is a factor, many inferences are made and somehow become "common knowledge." However, a lot of times, those ideas and misconceptions are entirely untrue, only adding to the confusion and misunderstandings around these conditions. ADHD is no different. Before getting your diagnosis, you might have had some of those misconceptions. Additionally, if you're only being diagnosed now as an adult, maybe it never came up before because your parents fell into those myths about ADHD and didn't think you met the criteria.

This section is going to cover some of the common myths for children and adults with ADHD as well as a little information about the reality of the situation.

The first myth about ADHD we'll discuss is that everyone with ADHD is hyperactive. Hyperactivity is more commonly seen in children than adults, but even in kids, it isn't a universal symptom. A lot of children who have ADHD but are not hyperactive simply appear spaced out and aloof.

Another myth of ADHD is that people with it can never pay attention. While inattention is a common symptom of ADHD, there are times when it can be circumstantial. The reason that ADHD is commonly associated with trouble at school or work is because of the nature of inattention with this neurological disorder. It is easy to focus on a task or activity that is interesting and engaging to the individual.

In fact, children and adults with ADHD can develop a hyperfocus on the activities and subjects that they enjoy and find interesting, shutting the rest of the world out and losing track of time. Inattention might only come in at school and work when the material is not engaging, leading to boredom and mind-wandering.

Myth number three is more related to children, but can be applied to adults as well. The myth is that those with ADHD could behave better if they wanted to. Fortunately with the growing field of psychology, this is a less stigmatized myth. It does still exist though. No matter how they try, children and adults might literally be unable to sit still or be quiet. It is important to understand that this isn't purposeful acting out.

Myth number four is that children will grow out of their ADHD. Since this book is about adult ADHD, we've already covered this myth. However, for parents that told their children they'd grow out of it, or expected their children to grow out of it, accept the reality they might not.

Our fifth myth is another reason this book is going to be beneficial. This myth is that medication is the best way to treat ADHD. While medication is usually prescribed or recommended, it isn't always the best option. The best treatment options include education, behavioral therapy, exercise, nutrition, and support from friends, family, and the professional or school setting.

Chapter four and five are going to discuss self-care options like nutrition and exercise in more detail. However, these methods are considered more effective and beneficial because they help you as a whole, not just "covering up" the symptoms with medication. Thus you can live a successful life without being on medication forever.

Our sixth myth is about ADHD being a legitimate medical condition. Because of the confusion between normal childhood behavior and ADHD symptoms, there are a lot of people, and even medical professionals, that do not accept ADHD as a medical condition. Fortunately, the Center for Disease Control and the American Psychiatric Association do recognize it as a medical condition. It can even be tracked as a hereditary disorder; more on that in a later chapter section.

The seventh myth is somewhat similar to a previous myth. Myth seven is that people with ADHD just need to try harder (similar to being able to control their behavior). ADHD is not the result of laziness or lack of motivation. The concept of asking an adult or child with ADHD to "try to focus harder" is just like asking someone with the flu not to have a fever.

Myth eight is that only boys have ADHD. While boys and adult men more commonly have ADHD, it is not a gender- or sex-specific disorder. The way the medical field is organized, girls are more likely to be misdiagnosed, especially after puberty with menstrual and reproductive hormones, or be passed over all together. This discrepancy is usually because boys tend to present with more hyperactivity and impulsivity than girls. This isn't always the case, but it has influenced how ADHD is diagnosed across genders.

Myth number nine is that ADHD is a learning disability. While symptoms can get in the way of learning or cause trouble at work or school, people with ADHD do not necessarily have any trouble learning. The major difference is that learning disabilities are often related to specific areas, such as math, spatial awareness, or writing. It is possible to have ADHD and a learning disability, but they aren't interchangeable.

Our tenth myth, and probably one of the most misunderstood, or easiest to fall into, is that ADHD is the result of bad parenting. ADHD is neurological. While it can be a result of environmental factors, this does not include "bad parenting." Children with ADHD might be perceived as having no discipline, not get attention at home, or be hyperactive because their parents let them watch TV all day at home and they don't get their energy out.

These common judgments can make it even more difficult for parents with children who have ADHD. Additionally, it is incredibly frustrating for parents who are raising children with ADHD. That frustration can leak out in the public eye and easily be labeled as "bad parenting" and the child is considered a 'victim.' People with ADHD are not victims; they have a legitimate medical condition that is the result of neurons, not parenting.

Signs and Symptoms

Some of the symptoms and signs of ADHD have been discussed throughout the chapter. Here we will break down those symptoms to show just how they can manifest and what the results are. We will also go over how certain symptoms in children may change or evolve in adulthood, presenting differently.

It is important to remember that, even with a general consistency in symptoms, everyone is different. Every brain is different, even ones with ADHD. As you look over the symptoms, you might recognize certain manifestations in yourself, giving yourself more clarity into your behavior and thought patterns. Others might seem completely off base.

The three major symptoms in ADHD can present in a lot of different ways, so you might even be experiencing these symptoms and not even realizing it based on the common definition. It can be hard to face up to certain behaviors and responses. This section is not meant to spark self-reflection in your actions and reactions. However, if you do start making connections, that is only going to help you grow and learn to manage your ADHD.

Inattention

Inattention is one of those symptoms that isn't constant. It can be very circumstantial, presenting only at times when the individual is trudging through something they don't enjoy or find boring. Yet, when it comes to tasks they like, focus comes easily and naturally.

Another type of inattention is not being able to stay on task. This kind of inattention usually results in someone with ADHD jumping around. They will start something, then leave it unfinished and move onto something else. A lot of projects get started, but might never get finished. Or, they need to jump around and will eventually circle back to the original project to complete it.

Common traits of inactivity include:

- Poor attention to detail

- Having trouble focusing, being easily distracted

- Makes careless mistakes and can't pay close attention

- Difficulty starting and/or finishing tasks or projects

- Doesn't seem to listen when spoken to

- Can't focus, even when playing

- Can't regulate attention

- Can't follow instructions, or has difficulty remembering instructions

- Can't finish schoolwork, career work, or chores consistently

- Forgetful

- Can't stay organized or plan ahead

- Avoidance of disliked tasks, especially ones that require mental effort

- Poor time management skills

- Loses track of things like schoolwork, keys, books, or daily items

- Forgetting to do chores and daily activities

Impulsivity

Being impulsive often leads to a lack of control of the body and general self-control issues. People with ADHD don't censor themselves very well, leading to conversation interruptions, invading people's personal space, and asking irrelevant questions on a topic being discussed or in class.

Impulsivity can lead to tactlessness, moodiness, and difficulty with instructions like "be patient." They can come off as overactive, especially with emotions. This can cause others to view that person as needy, weird, or disrespectful.

Common instances of impulsivity include:

- Fidgeting

- Acting without thinking

- Tapping hands or feet, squirming when sitting still

- Restlessness

- Guessing answers rather than solving the problem or thinking of the correct answer

- Blurts out answers or interrupts conversations

- Put themselves in risky or dangerous situations that risk their safety

- Excessive talking

- Intrudes on the games or activities of others without being invited

- Isn't always appropriate in what they say, especially when it comes to appropriate timing

- Can't control powerful emotions, resulting in tantrums or overzealous expressions that invade the privacy and personal space of others

- Can't wait their turn

Hyperactivity

There is a fair amount of overlap between hyperactivity and impulsivity. In adults, hyperactivity is rarer or might present in different ways. It might appear more like impulsive tendencies than hyperactivity. While hyperactivity is commonly associated with constant motion, it isn't the only way hyperactivity can manifest.

Hyperactive thoughts can also be present in ADHD, and are also more common than physical hyperactivity in adults with ADHD. Sometimes adults don't outgrow hyperactivity so much as having it become a more internal process of a constant stream of thoughts and being unable to turn their mind off.

Both adults and children with hyperactivity are likely to try to multitask, but at a pace they can't keep up with themselves. Both probably tap feet, pencils, or fidget in one way or another when they are expected to sit still.

Common signs of hyperactivity include:

- Squirming and fidgeting when trying to sit still, constantly adjusting their position when trying to relax

- Can't relax

- Constantly on the go and in motion

- Likes to run around, climb on objects, even when inappropriate

- Takes unnecessary risks with activities such as in skateboarding, climbing, or sports

- Talking excessively, or talking a lot in at a very fast pace

- Short temper

- Always has new ideas, plans, and goals, but no follow through

- Low frustration tolerance

- Inability to regulate emotions

Child Symptoms Translated to Adult Symptoms

Some of the symptoms that are common in ADHD in children do present in adulthood, only they change over time. Maybe they evolve with age and maturity, or maybe you just navigate them differently. Sometimes they change based on circumstances.

In children, failing in school or being a chronic underachiever are often symptoms of ADHD. This is usually related to inattention and hyperactivity. However, in adulthood, this becomes unemployment or lack of success in work. That could mean anything from not being able to hold down a job to not being able to advance in your career.

Injuries in children with ADHD are common. Through impulsivity and hyperactivity, kids will take unnecessary risks, putting their safety in jeopardy. As a result, they get frequent injuries. In adulthood, this can still translate to physical injury in terms of car crashes from inattention or impulsivity. It can also lead to risk taking with finances, career, or your own health or safety.

Drug experimentation can be very common with adolescents who have ADHD. In youths, drug experimentation usually stems from a need for freedom or escape combined with impulsivity and curiosity. If they feel more 'normal' with substances, then this can develop into substance addiction. For adults, it can carry over from youth or develop as a result of wanting to self-medicate or escape from perceived failures and become a substance use disorder.

Two disorders that children are prone to, especially children with ADHD, are oppositional defiant disorder and conduct disorder. Both have symptoms of rebelliousness, inability to follow instructions, stubbornness, and conflicts with authority. In adulthood, these disorders can lead to, or evolve into, criminal and gang activity. They can also become antisocial personality disorder, which cannot be diagnosed in anyone under the age of eighteen.

Children can be very impulsive and careless with symptoms of ADHD. In adulthood, there are consequences that come with carelessness and impulsivity. These can be extreme, like unwanted pregnancy or contracting an STD. It could also be in regard to making extravagant purchases without considering finances or bills.

Repetitive failure is another byproduct of the symptoms of ADHD in children. This could be in school, sports, with friends, chores at home, etc. Failure could be in failing to complete a task, failing to succeed per the standards of the activity, and so forth. Adults can still experience this failure, but it can also cause a general sense of hopelessness, resignation, and frustration. As a result, adults might not strive to try anything new, thinking they won't ever succeed.

Risk Factors and Causes

While the causes and risk factors of ADHD are unknown as a whole, there are some risk factors that have been known to contribute. A cause is an actual reason for why someone experiences a condition or disorder. In this case, the exact causes of ADHD as a neurological disorder are unknown in the medical community.

A risk factor is a factor that can contribute to the development of ADHD. While it is generally considered a lifelong condition, there are very rare instances that ADHD can actually develop in adulthood. More often than not, adult ADHD was simply undiagnosed or missed in childhood. The factors in this chapter are to add to your education of ADHD for yourself, but also some considerations to have in regard to your own children or if you plan on having children.

Genetics and Hereditary

Even though the exact cause isn't known, there is a large link between ADHD and genetics. It is incredibly hereditary. More than 50% of adults that have ADHD end up having a child with ADHD. There are some genetic markers that have been more recently flagged in the scientific community that can be related to the development of ADHD.

Genetic factors and hereditary factors are beyond control. However, with genetics, like in most of science and medicine, there are no 100% outcomes. Your genetics are a result of recessive and dominant genes from both your parents, which are influenced by their parents and all the generations before them.

In some genetic instances, twins can occur every other generation in a family. Due to these inconsistencies, or what can't be tracked easily from one generation to the next, genetic factors are hard to pin down. That being said, there is plenty of evidence to show ADHD is hereditary in many instances.

Environmental

When it comes to environmental factors, this is a blanket term that can indicate any factor outside your body that you are exposed to. They can be natural, like pollen and apples, or they can be man-made like pesticides or paint. Sometimes environmental factors are only impactful if a child is exposed to them in utero or in very early life. Some environmental factors can be impactful throughout life.

Extreme stress and trauma are two environmental factors that have been related to the development of ADHD. These factors can happen in childhood or adulthood. However, the child psyche is often more fragile or susceptible to mind-altering trauma and stress.

Some toxins such as lead paint and bisphenol also correlate to the development of ADHD.

Environmental factors aren't necessarily responsible for the development of ADHD in children or adults who have a genetic predisposition for it (meaning it is present in their genetic history). Sometimes environmental factors can result in more severe symptoms of a preexisting condition, like ADHD.

Disruption of Development

The central nervous system can be impacted in childhood and adulthood. When the central nervous system is injured or traumatized, like with a brain injury or concussion, it can result in the development of neurological disorders, such as ADHD. This is the most common instance for an adult developing ADHD in adulthood.

However, it isn't limited to adulthood injuries. Premature birth and alcohol use during pregnancy can result in a child born with ADHD.

Chapter 2:
Living With Adult ADHD

Once you have your diagnosis, or even if you don't have a formal diagnosis but it has been suggested that you have adult ADHD, you might be curious about how exactly it impacts your life. The previous chapter covered symptoms and some of the areas in your life that can be impacted by those symptoms. This chapter is going to elaborate further on how adults ADHD can affect you and your daily life, as well as some tips and tricks that can be used to help you in specific areas.

Even though ADHD behavior is neurological and it is considered 'outside' the control of those who have ADHD, that doesn't mean you can't manage it or overcome some of the more severe symptoms. If you've been living with adult ADHD and only just got a diagnosis, you may have felt like something is off for a while, but could never put all the pieces together. Knowing the truth is only the first step, because there is a certain amount of responsibility that you are going to have to take in order to lead a more successful life that isn't ruled by your ADHD.

Living With Undiagnosed Adult ADHD

A lot of adults living with undiagnosed ADHD feel like they are always "running on empty." No matter how hard they try, they can't get organized, manage their time, or discipline themselves. It can be even worse when friends and family point out these 'shortcomings' as well, leading to feelings of inadequacy. This struggle leads to a constant mental and emotional exhaustion that can lead to dread and depression when trying to face every new day. Without knowing the cause of these struggles, it can feel hopeless to even keep trying.

Adults who have been living with ADHD without knowing it usually feel 'different.' They might get told they are lazy, that they aren't trying hard enough, that they are too spacey, etc. You're left with this overall feeling that you can't reach your own potential, and others likely point this out as well. It can leave you with a disconnected feeling like you don't belong.

Sometimes, undiagnosed ADHD can leave adults with a feeling of paranoia, like others are watching them closely, don't trust them, or are laughing behind their backs. This paranoia is usually a result of adults with ADHD not being taken seriously by their peers, or feeling inadequate next to their peers.

There are a lot of adults who thought they were living a normal life. They had on metaphorical blinders to what 'normal' was. They might have neglected their finances, housekeeping, and maintaining a job, all while indulging in excessive reading, video game playing, or something else. To them, it seemed normal. It can be very sobering to discover that neurotypical adults generally don't usually live that way. When the blinders come off and the truth is revealed, the struggle becomes even worse!

Some children don't have the typical symptoms of struggling in school or other symptoms that would lead to a diagnosis. Therefore, they are able to slip through the cracks and progress through their education and development somewhat normally. Unfortunately, as they enter into adulthood, things might begin to happen that make success more difficult. Often, in the workforce, individuals are given a certain amount of self-management. With undiagnosed ADHD this can lead to missing deadlines, not finishing projects, and otherwise stumbling over all kinds of roadblocks that become setbacks.

There is a common feeling of "winging it" among adults with undiagnosed ADHD—the feeling of just flying by the seat of your pants to make it through every moment of every day. You don't have a plan; you feel like you don't know what you are doing. Everyone has a breaking point though, and "winging it" can feel very frustrating.

Another common metaphor for adults who have been struggling with ADHD and not knowing it is that they feel like their life's a puzzle that doesn't fit. They can see and touch all the pieces, and know what pieces they want to go together, but the pieces just don't fit! They can't store the correct information in their mind to make everything work out how they envisioned it.

Boredom is a symptom of adult ADHD. It can actually lead to people frequently leaving jobs because the work becomes mundane and uninteresting. The same thing can happen in personal relationships. Without knowing the source of this boredom, it is easy to blame others, saying the job wasn't stimulating enough, or any other excuse. It can be very difficult to keep anything in your life long term with that ever outlying boredom waiting to swoop in and make your life uninteresting.

Adults with ADHD can become incredibly overwhelmed. This can happen at work, at school, in the grocery store, while walking in a crowded street, anywhere. Being that overwhelmed can lead to the desire to run and hide. It can result in quitting jobs, dropping out of school, avoiding social situations, and keeping yourself locked away.

Shame is another feeling that is present in adults who don't know they are struggling with ADHD. It can be so hard to not compare yourself to others. If you see your friends and neighbors succeeding while you can't get that promotion at work, can't manage that house, or struggle to raise your children, feelings of shame can become quite prominent and discouraging. Not being able to do what is 'expected' can become a huge source of shame for a lot of individuals, especially if they have a house or family to look after.

An inability to manage finances has also been discussed as a trait that adults with ADHD struggle with. They can never save enough money, fall into impulse buys, and are constantly paying bills as they go without a budget or plan. They've tried the spreadsheet, tried automatic payments, and written up a budget, but they can't get their finances organized.

Another major struggle of living with adult ADHD, especially when it is undiagnosed, is that the people around you don't understand it either. You may be perceived as lazy, unmotivated, irresponsible, flighty, and aloof. None of these traits are inherently negative; however, they can be seen as negative by others. Once others begin to apply these labels to you, it is hard to see yourself differently.

You become a self-fulfilling prophecy, because it can become easier to just be what everyone says you are rather than struggle to not be how they see you. Plus, if you don't know what is wrong, there is no reasoning or explanation you can give that will change their mind. Even with a diagnosis of adult ADHD, a lot of people in your life still might not understand.

You may have been struggling with any number of these situations, never knowing why or knowing the source. The worst part of having undiagnosed ADHD is experiencing all these feelings and struggles, but not having an answer as to why! Everything you might try to offer as an explanation just becomes an excuse, and people don't want to hear excuses. Fortunately, now you have your answer and you can begin working through it.

What to Do With a Diagnosis

When you receive your diagnosis, there are a lot of strong emotions that can accompany this revelation. You might be able to relate with some of those strong emotions. First, you need to understand your feelings on having adult ADHD before you can decide what you can do with that information. Three of the most commonly felt emotions after this diagnosis are relief, anger, and sadness. Do you remember how you felt when you were told that you have adult ADHD? Like the stages of grief, you might even cycle through the different emotions, trying to work them out in your mind.

Relief

Relief comes from a sense of happiness at having a name to give the reason behind your struggles and your symptoms. It can be very validating to know that there is in fact a reason for what you've been experiencing and that you aren't any of the names or labels that people have given you.

You might also feel a great sense of relief when you are given documentation and literature that better describes your symptoms. This process can be quite uplifting, because you'll be able to start understanding why certain things haven't been working.

Another source of relief can come from the prospect of medication and treatment. Knowing that ADHD is treatable and manageable can give you a sense of hope and safety. You'll be able to take necessary steps to manage your symptoms and turn yourself around, so to speak. Hope is powerful.

With a diagnosis, a lot of new doors open up for you as well. You're able to pursue your own education and research, with books like this for helping yourself. With so much online activity, you can find communities and forums of other people that have had similar experiences as you. By finding that kind of support, you can feel like you belong, like you are being seen in a way that you never were before. Without a diagnosis, you can't connect with other people that have gone through what you went through, and knowing you aren't alone can be quite a relief.

Anger

Medical diagnoses are not always what someone wants. Mental health diagnoses are even less accepted because of the stigmas that surround them. Anger can manifest in a few different ways. You might be angry because you don't want to have ADHD. You might get frustrated to have a mental health condition that you are going to have for your whole life!

Sometimes knowing the truth doesn't make you feel better, because you know it is going to take a lot of work and effort to pull through and overcome this particular trial.

Anger can also come out directed at other people. Maybe you'll feel angry towards your parents, teachers, former romantic partners, or former employers for the way they treated you in their misunderstanding of you. While it isn't entirely their fault, because they didn't know, the anger can still come out.

Depending on the culture or environment you are raised in, ADHD symptoms could have led to blame, emotional abuse, and a lot of ridicule and insult from the people in your childhood who were supposed to support you. Finding out it isn't your fault can cause that repressed or 'swallowed' anger to resurface.

You might even feel angry at yourself. Again, having ADHD isn't within your control, but you might feel angry that you didn't go to a doctor or seek help sooner. That self-anger can come from a long time of not understanding what was wrong.

Extreme emotions are a part of ADHD, so it is not surprising that this intense feeling of anger can come from a medical diagnosis of adult ADHD.

Sadness

Another strong emotion that can be felt intensely from ADHD and an inability to regulate emotions is sadness. This is a complicated emotion when it comes to a medical diagnosis because it can apply to a lot of the same feelings that stirred your anger.

You could feel sad about having a lifelong condition to manage. You could feel sad that you didn't get diagnosed or seek help sooner. Sometimes you'll feel anger first, and then that anger becomes sadness once the initial shock wears off.

Sadness can be the result of mourning the life or future you could have had without ADHD. You might even feel sadness for your younger self, or past self, for all the struggles they had to endure without any answers.

With a diagnosis come a lot of different treatment options like medication, behavioral therapy, and self-management. Sadness can accompany the realization that you might never have a 'normal' like that doesn't include some constant reminder that you have ADHD and that you aren't neurotypical.

Anger and sadness are very closely related when it comes to extreme emotions. Oftentimes, anger is the defensive action when you really are sad but don't want to face the sadness. So, you might have already phased from anger to sadness. Then again, you might still be struggling to determine what you are feeling. Don't be too surprised if sadness creeps up on you at some point.

What to Do After Initial Diagnosis

The best thing to do for yourself when you are still in the midst of the intense emotions around your diagnosis is to reassure yourself. Emotions are natural. They are a coping mechanism, and they are a part of being human. Even though it might not seem like it, emotions serve a purpose, and the way you feel them is telling you something. It might be painful to remind yourself that emotions are natural, but you can feel better knowing they are.

If you have friends or a close family member that you feel comfortable with, talk to them about what you are feeling and going through. Having their support and comfort can be very therapeutic and helpful as you absorb this new information about yourself.

Look for an ADHD support group. You can look for an in-person group in your area, or connect to an online group. By connecting with other people who have similar experiences, you can feel validated in what you are feeling and going through, but also have a source of information and support from people that understand.

If you are open to therapy, look around for a therapist that has experience working with adults with ADHD. Even if they aren't a behavioral therapist, just having someone to talk to who can help guide you is going to be very helpful and enlightening.

Remember that you don't need to tell everyone. Not everyone in your life is going to be accepting of or understand ADHD and the symptoms that you have. You might find it helpful to discuss the details with your employer, or your direct superior. That could give you a little relief at work.

If you're in school, telling your teachers or professors is a good way to get them to work with you and help manage your curriculum around your symptoms. Eventually, you'll want to work out how to manage this on your own, but in the beginning, you might need that extra support.

When it comes to a romantic partner, it can be beneficial to the relationships to tell them about your diagnosis. However, this is only if you trust them, feel comfortable with them, and think that they will support you and be understanding. You aren't telling them as an excuse, but as a way to navigate potential pitfalls. If you're living with your romantic partner, it is probably a good idea to tell them.

Be as selective as you want with who you tell. As a medical diagnosis, ADHD is entirely your own business, and you can keep it that way if you want. If you do have people in your life that want to be supportive, give them information and literature about ADHD so they can educate themselves and help you in their own way.

It is important to let all your health care providers know about your diagnosis and any treatments you are pursuing. This way, they won't introduce any conflicting treatments or medications.

Managing Adult ADHD Symptoms

While there are ADHD medications that have been successful in treating ADHD in adults, the best way to cope with symptoms is to manage them. Managing symptoms is different from treating them. It isn't the same as holistic treatments or natural treatments either. Managing symptoms comes down to the lifestyle changes you can institute so that you can live day to day without being controlled by your ADHD.

There are a few myths about adult ADHD and how to properly manage it. One such myth is that medication is the only way to treat ADHD effectively. Medication isn't a cure, nor is it the only solution. Long-term use of medications can result in other problems as well, which is why lifelong and chronic conditions should be managed as organically as possible.

Some people fall into the stigma of ADHD and think that they are too lazy or unintelligent to help themselves. These are unfortunately labels that are the byproduct of having ADHD and being undiagnosed, but you aren't actually any of those things. ADHD is a disorder that can be a hindrance for normal functions, but you don't lack those qualities.

Western medicine does like to be at the center of all treatment plans and options when it comes to conditions and disorders. This leads a lot of people to believe that a medical professional can cure them or solve all their ADHD problems. Honestly, this is not the case. Health care professionals can really only do so much. The rest is up to you. You can make the most significant changes.

The most disheartening myth about ADHD management, and the one that usually leads to anger from a diagnosis, is thinking that ADHD is a life sentence and you'll never be able to overcome your symptoms. Sure, there is no cure for ADHD, and the symptoms will probably follow you around your whole life, but you are a powerful individual who can make the choice to work towards a different future. With a little commitment and establishing of patterns and coping mechanisms, you'll see you can improve your symptoms and live quite 'normally.'

Depending on the aspect of your life, there are different tips, tricks, and strategies for managing ADHD symptoms.

Work and School

Focus and productivity are a real challenge in school or at work for adults with ADHD. You are usually given tasks all day long, and in some instances expected to take extra work home with you. The goal is to work with your strengths and minimize the impact of your ADHD symptoms.

Tips and tricks for staying productive and task oriented at work or school include:

- Organize your desk or space every day. Set aside a little time at the beginning or end of your work or school day to organize your space. Declutter unneeded papers by discarding or filing them. Put all your pencils and writing utensils away; stack up your books and files.

- Color code your lists. The same as you use lists in organization and prioritization, use them at work too. Use colored markers, pens, or sticky notes to prioritize and organize your tasks for school and work. If you have to take notes, color code them as well based on topic, importance, or relevance.

- Use your lists and color coding to prioritize tasks and projects.

- Minimize distractions by sitting front and center at meetings, in training, or in lectures. Move away from people that talk and closer to the speaker if possible.

- Keep your desk facing a wall rather than a door to minimize your exposure to external commotion. If you have an office, keep the door closed. If you have windows, put the blinds down. Close out of all internet and social media applications. Put your phone on airplane mode or turn it off so you don't get any notifications.

- Keep a notebook on hand to write down any big ideas or amazing revelations and save them for later. Come back to them when your tasks are done.

- Maximize your attention span. If possible, record meetings, lectures, or training, or ask for a recording of it from the speaker. You can go back to it whenever you need to. If you can't get a recording, maybe you can get a written transcript.

- Repeat directions. When someone gives you instructions, repeat them back to make sure you are both in understanding and to help you remember them. You might want to write them down too.

- Let yourself move around. Take periodic stretch, snack, or walking breaks, but only give yourself about five to 10 minutes before returning to work—just long enough to clear out the cobwebs and get some fidgets out. Use a timer to keep track of time for your breaks.

Relationships

Maintaining romantic relationships can be difficult for adults with ADHD. Even friendships and familial relationships can be hard. This comes from ADHD symptoms resulting in frustration, extreme emotional outbursts, and a general inability to regulate emotions. Most of these suggestions are about romantic relationships, but they can be applied to friend and family relationships as well.

Some good habits to form to help maintain relationships include:

- Working on communication. This is a lifelong skill for everyone to learn, including adults with ADHD. Discover how you best communicate and then practice communicating with your friends, family, and romantic partners to establish a strong flow of understanding. This reduces misunderstandings and miscommunication, limiting frustration and situations that can result in angry outbursts.

- Build teamwork. Set a plan with your romantic partner to establish equality in what needs to get done. Break up chores, responsibilities, and other joint efforts. You don't have to handle everything on your own, and you can stick to the responsibilities that speak to your strengths. For example, it might be best for a neurotypical partner to manage your joint finances.

- Create a routine. You and your partner should establish a routine that works for both of you. Depending on your work and lifestyle, you might have a couple different routines. You might have separate workday routines, but similar nighttime routines, and then a whole different routine on weekends. Routines set expectations for what needs to get done and how your day is going to flow with your partner and on your own time.

- Communicate with friends and family. If you're running late, let them know. Don't be afraid to say no to them. Plan for activities you know you can handle so you can enjoy your time with them without getting overwhelmed.

- We'll talk about relationships in detail in the next chapter.

Personal Organization and Controlling Clutter

Inattention and distractibility can lead to a lack of organization and clutter in the home. Chores get forgotten or left incomplete, eventually piling up. Over time, the prospect of catching up becomes so daunting and overwhelming, it gets avoided, adding more to the clutter and disorganization.

You'll want to first start by organizing your home. Maybe take it one room at a time, but organize the space, and then keep it organized.

Tips for avoiding clutter and disorganization include:

- Get in the habit of writing and keeping lists for EVERYTHING. To-do lists, shopping lists, organization plan lists, chore lists, projects, deadlines, literally everything. There are phone apps and computer programs that are easy to use for list making.

- Create space by figuring out what you need among your possessions every day. Invest in some storage bins and pack away the things that you don't need regularly. You might want to label the bins by how frequently you might need the items and put similar items together so you can find them easier when the time comes.

- Get yourself a calendar app or day planner. Put everything in your schedule. This includes meal times, work times, play time, when you exercise, when you sleep, etc. Make your schedule as airtight as possible, and factor in travel time when needed. If you can, set notifications on your calendar, or alarms, so you know when it is time to transition. If you're using a daily planner, put your lists with the planner so they are all together.

- Stick to a "deal with it now" mentality. You kick your shoes off when you get into the front door, immediately put them on the shoe rack, don't let them "sit until later." You got up from the couch and threw the throw blanket you were using aside. Turn around and fold the blanket; don't tell yourself you'll get back to it later. You missed the trashcan when throwing a balled-up piece of paper in it; go over and pick it up, don't wait until the next time you have something to throw away. If something can be done in two minutes or less, do it immediately; don't put it off.

- Go paperless and/or develop a filing system. Deal with paper as it comes, such as mail. Don't let those papers pile up and be forgotten.

- Label everything. Have designated spots for your keys, shoes, jacket, purse, textbooks, etc. Then label those places so you have the visual reminder that there is always supposed to be something in that space. If there isn't, find the item and put it in its spot right away.

Managing Finances and Bills

Adults with ADHD are at risk of impulse buying and not being able to manage their finances properly. Establish good spending habits and bill-paying habits to overcome that.

Some bill management and finance management habits to employ include:

- Use online banking. You can have your finances available on your phone or computer so they are easy to pull up at any time. You can track money coming in and money going out and pay bills directly. You can also set up automatic bill payments so that you don't forget to pay. The money for bills has to be in your account though.

- Set up reminders to pay bills. Have notifications, alarms, and notations on your calendar for when bills are due. You should also include the amount of the bill so that you can plan ahead. You might want to set a reminder for when the bill is due, and a reminder a few days before.

- Track your finances. There are a lot of apps that you can use to help plan a budget and manage your finances. Take advantage of those to easily track your spending.

- Stop impulse buying by shopping with cash only. Parting with cash is harder than using a debit/credit card or a check.

- Only have one emergency credit card and get rid of the rest. When shopping, keep a calculator open with a running total of how much you've spent. Don't let that number get above a predetermined limit.

- Avoid stores and shops where you know you spend too much or are likely to overspend.

Time Management and Staying on Schedule

Losing track of time, getting distracted, or getting too immersed in something is common with adults who have ADHD. It is important to develop a sense of time awareness.

Tips to manage time and stay on schedule include:

- Get in the habit of checking clocks. Have a clock in every room of your house and put it somewhere where you can see it easily from anywhere in the room. Set a time for every five minutes, and then look at the clock when the timer goes off. Build the habit of watching clocks and knowing the time.

- With your calendar app on your phone, clock app, or a simple kitchen timer, set timers. The phone apps are nice because you can put a label on the alarm to tell you what comes next. For longer tasks, set timers and alarms in intervals to help remind you to stay on task.

- Give yourself more time than you think you need. ADHD makes it difficult to estimate the right time allotment. Always overestimate so you don't get in a tight spot.

- When you have to be somewhere, like work, an appointment, or a meeting, plan to be there early. Put it in your calendar for five or 10 minutes earlier than necessary. Set your alarms the same way. This will help you not be late.

- Prioritize tasks with a list, writing down what has to be done and then using numbers, or another system, to plan which order you will be completing them in.

- Take projects one at a time. Don't let yourself move on until you finish one task to completion; otherwise you probably won't come back to it.

Learn to say no. Don't take on more than you can handle, and set boundaries for yourself. This is very difficult to do, even for neurotypical people. Learning to say no can literally change your life!

Chapter 3:
Adult ADHD & Relationships

Living with ADHD can be quite difficult, especially when it comes to relationships. In this chapter, we will discuss how this might influence your relationships with not just your partner, but also your friends and family. We will take a quick look at how you may be able to work around these obstacles, how to counteract some of the reactions from others, and how to improve your relationships overall.

What to Expect

Here we will highlight a few problems you might come to expect from relationships involving someone with ADHD and how to resolve those issues as best you can.

Distraction

You are probably already aware of the most common symptom in many sufferers of ADHD, and that is being distracted all the time. This may lead to numerous complications in everyday life, but most importantly, it can lead any relationship into turmoil, and ultimately leave it in ruins.

Now, keep in mind this can be said for any relationship, let alone a relationship where someone who suffers from ADHD is involved.

Being distracted may lead to your friends thinking you have no interest in their lives and hobbies, ultimately causing a rift in the group, singling you out. When in a committed relationship, being distracted might cause several issues. Speaking from experience, when you seem uninterested in a discussion you are seemingly a part of, your partner might feel neglected, unimportant, and even undesired. These issues speak for themselves, and not surprisingly, they are problems every couple faces. When ADHD is added, however, the issue simply becomes more severe. However, it can be alleviated by discussing your current state with your group of friends and/or partner.

This is an easy way to help your loved ones understand why you might seem distant or distracted. Simply explaining to someone that you suffer from ADHD can make a tremendous difference in their attitude toward you.

Some people might find it difficult to reveal such private information to their friends for fear of being ridiculed or stigmatized. Some individuals even go as far as to say that you are lying or simply making up excuses. This is unfortunate, but do you really need those types of friends in your life anyway?

The best way to come forth with such information is usually in a straightforward manner. When you meet someone new who you are certain you will interact with again, simply put it out there; they will understand in time. Relationships are a two-way street, after all.

Being forgetful

So, the time has arrived. You have been together in this partnership for a whole year, and as with many new relationships, expectations are high. Your partner looks at you with a confused look that slowly turns to anger or maybe sadness. You forgot your first year anniversary; that is a biggie.

Forgetfulness is, unfortunately, a symptom of many conditions ranging from ADHD to old age. It can be forgiven from time to time; however, should you forget a few too many times, it may become problematic not just in your relationship with your partner, but ones with friends and family as well.

If you forget to do a favor for a loved one, it may leave them feeling like they cannot depend on you. Reliability is hard to come by in modern times, and ADHD may affect your ability to be the most reliable individual possible. Luckily, in the last few years, society has become a bit more understanding of these types of disorders. Also, with the help of technology, there are many ways you can counter this issue and become more reliable than some of your friends ever were themselves.

When dealing with forgetfulness, be it as a symptom of ADHD or for any other reason, it is always best to make note of something the moment you are informed of it. Say you and your partner decide you want to go on a romantic outing a month from now; make either a physical or digital note so you avoid forgetting.

Later, we will discuss scheduling and organization. This will help you with more than just remembering, but also with setting up a good support system for daily life in general.

Hyper-focus

When you do something that interests you, you get completely immersed in it; it becomes your sole point of focus and existence. This is what it means to be hyper-focused. It's pretty self-explanatory, but surprisingly, not everyone knows that this is a symptom of ADHD.

Being hyper-focused is not exclusively associated with ADHD, and it does not necessarily present itself as a negative thing. In a relationship with someone you love, however, it might become a problem.

When hyper-focused, a person develops something akin to tunnel vision—not physically, but metaphorically. They will block everything out except that which is the object of their focus, leaving their partner outside that tunnel, feeling left out or neglected. When dealing with hyper-focus, it can become quite difficult, as one does not always realize when they enter this state.

In order to help your partner or friends understand this, make sure they know what you like and what your hobbies are. This can provide them with some insight, as they will soon realize when these things are in conversation or in front of you, you tend to cut them out, giving them the sign that they might have to remind you of their existence.

This specific state does differ from person to person; some might be easily shaken from their trance, while others may require a more physical reminder of the world around them. Find what works best for you, and discuss that with your partner.

Impulsivity

To a certain extent, there are many people who suffer from being impulsive. Whether it is due to ADHD or any other form of a disorder, in the end, it can lead to the same thing: a problematic relationship. Impulsivity can lead you to express certain thoughts during an argument without thinking it through. This can have devastating effects on a relationship, because you might not have meant what you said, but ultimately, it was still heard.

Being impulsive may lead to you spending an exorbitant amount of money on something simply because it caught your fancy, and when you do not have any money to spend, you will most likely use credit cards. This can affect a relationship severely, especially when married, as the debt can pile up, leaving your partner to suffer great stress. Even when you have the money, it can be nerve-racking to have a large amount of junk around the house cluttering every room, especially if your partner has OCD.

Impulsivity can lead to more dangerous outcomes as many ADHD patients push the limits of public safety. Some might drive recklessly, swerving through traffic or speeding on the highway, while others with the disorder might enjoy the impulsive thrill of sex in public areas or even the seductive thought of impulsive infidelity. The effects on relationships any of these impulsive moments can have are devastating.

Due to the very nature of this symptom, it is quite hard to deal with, even for people who do not suffer from ADHD. When in a relationship, it is always a good idea to think of your partner when you feel an impulse taking over. What might they think? How might they react or feel?

Another way to cope is to have something to which you can direct your impulsive energy toward; something as basic as a water bottle can help. Taking a sip of water when you get that feeling or fidgeting with it in your hands seems simple, but making it a habit can save you from saying something you might regret.

One last thing to try is to avoid situations that you know might trigger or lead to impulsive behavior.

Procrastination

This is an issue many people deal with. Unfortunately, some ADHD patients do not have the luxury of choice in the matter. An example might be when your partner asks you to do something simple like move a box, and you procrastinate and soon forget, becoming focused on the task you are currently busy with. Then, night falls, and your partner is disappointed that you did not complete the simple task they requested of you.

Procrastinating can lead to more severe outcomes as well. Perhaps you had a project at work to complete for which you had a deadline, but you decided to leave it for another day. When that day comes, you might have to deal with unexpected circumstances, leaving you stressed and frustrated; you might even lose your job altogether because you could not complete the project in time.

Dealing with this symptom is fairly easy, in a manner of speaking. Do what needs to be done the moment you are aware of it; if it cannot be done immediately, add it to your schedule and stick to it. This is simple enough and quite effective. We will discuss scheduling in the following chapter in more detail.

Mood swings

When dealing with a person who suffers from ADHD, you might notice their strange moods from time to time. One moment, you will be watching a movie together, happy as can be, and the next moment, they might get angry or sad at something seemingly insignificant. When you are the one experiencing the mood swings, it can be quite confusing as well. When something small triggers a big emotion, it can be very frustrating, especially when you are in a relationship.

You might be enjoying a memorable moment with your partner when a small leaf is gently carried into your face by a light breeze, triggering an immense fit of rage at this small inconvenience. It can startle your partner quite a bit, resulting in them feeling as if they cannot relax around you. Walking on eggshells all day can be exhausting and can lead to a pile of smaller problems in a relationship. An inevitable crash of mixed emotions from both sides will be the end result if your mood swings are extreme.

Due to mood swings being so erratic, it's hard to pinpoint a specific treatment or counter for these reactions. The best you can do is try and lessen them by exercising regularly, making sure you have a balanced diet, and getting enough sleep. Some people have found meditation to help as well, but should you have severe mood swings, it's best to consult a professional in order to reach a more permanent solution.

Relationships Are Still Relationships

In the end, you and your partner are in it together, so communication is the key that will unlock a beautiful and sustainable life with each other.

If you are the one suffering from ADHD, be sure to inform your partner of this; do not be discouraged to share this personal information as it will form a stronger bond between you. If your partner is the one diagnosed with ADHD, do some research on the disorder, and make sure to tell them you are willing to work with them and that you understand the current situation. This will make them more confident, and it might end up helping both of you alleviate some of the symptoms.

Remember not to use ADHD as an excuse for your actions. Yes, you are suffering from a disorder, but this does not give you exemption from problems you are causing. Take the initiative, take responsibility for your actions, and make sure to acknowledge when you made a mistake. Work toward fixing that mistake, and make it clear to your partner that you intend to do so.

This does not mean, however, that all responsibility falls on the individual with ADHD. The partner who is not suffering from ADHD should never play the blame game. You have to acknowledge that sometimes it is not their fault. They cannot always control the outcome of this disorder, so find ways to deal with these symptoms together using patience and understanding.

Chapter 4:
Getting Organized & Structuring Daily Life

In modern times, there are many things we have to remember, many things we have to prepare for, and even more things we cannot possibly account for; and for someone with ADHD, this can be very discouraging. You might feel left behind as if your week started off badly and is seemingly getting worse as you try and figure out how it all got so out of hand in the first place. Missed appointments, forgotten promises, lost time, and skipped dates become norms that you cannot seem to escape.

Do not let this lifestyle be your only option as there are ways to improve your daily life. This will, in turn, improve your week, landing you in a relaxing weekend instead of somewhere playing catch-up with everything you missed.

Let's take a look at how you can build a structure for your day, organize your life, and improve your mental health as someone suffering from ADHD.

Organization Is Key

When going through life with ADHD, you will need a controlled environment to start your day, making the rest of your waking hours, as well as your week, go smoothly.

Your home is where you must feel the most comfortable, and having it organized properly can set the mood for your day. This may seem trivial, but it is a known symptom of ADHD to have things disorganized—and creating a chaotic atmosphere is the last thing you need. Eating, sleeping, and relaxing in a controlled environment will provide you with the mental strength to go meet the chaotic world that's out there.

The same place every time

Let's start off with the basics. You need to place all your belongings in the same location *every single time*. This is a great way to keep things organized. First off, establish specific areas to place your items such as counters, tabletops, key racks, bowls, storage areas, compartments, boxes, and shelves. You can put your keys, wallet, and anything else you might need to take with you when going out in their designated places.

Place any work-related items such as paperwork or your laptop on a specific desk or another surface every night. You can do this to avoid struggling every morning to find something, or it can prevent you from realizing you have forgotten something after already arriving at the office.

This goes for any other items in your living space as well. (Don't feel overwhelmed, though, as you don't have to redo your entire home in one day.)

Step by step

Take it step by step and room by room to organize everything, perhaps starting with your bedroom. Make sure your nightstands are not cluttered with things you do not need in your room, and make sure there is nothing on your bed except blankets and pillows. Try to split your clothing into sections so that they're not bundled together or in a heap. This will make life easier and also save you time in the morning when you're looking for something to wear for the day.

Spending less mental energy on finding something can help you regain focus on what is important. Many businessmen and women even go as far as buying multiple sets of the same clothing to wear every day so they do not waste any effort on deciding what to wear to work.

The bathroom

Moving along from your bedroom, the bathroom might be a good option. Making sure that the space you use to clean yourself is organized can make you feel even more refreshed. Some people clutter up their bathrooms with items placed on the basin, around the bathtub, on the cistern of their toilet, or on the floor of the shower.

This is far from ideal and can result in a chaotic morning as you rummage through everything. This could start your day off badly. Keep the edges of the bathtub clear of any items, and try to keep a small container hanging from the faucet or wall. The same goes for the basin; place the items in the medicine cabinet or cupboard below. If these storage areas are unavailable, get some plastic containers that you can place neatly against a wall or under the basin.

As for the shower, nothing should be on the floor as it can cause you to trip. Instead, you can mount a container against the wall or hang one from the faucet or top of the shower door. These small changes can result in your day starting off smoothly, without concern for bumping something over or tripping over a random object that fell to the floor.

Kitchen and living space

In your bathroom, you can follow the same guidelines as above. You should keep items neatly packed away and organized in order to avoid wasting time looking for something and getting annoyed in the process. The living room usually does not have much in it to organize, but something as simple as trying to find the TV remote can have a negative impact on a relaxing evening. Make sure to dedicate a specific space where you can store your remotes for digital devices. Make this clear to your friends when they visit, as well; it doesn't matter what they might think of it, because this is about you and how you can improve your life.

The kitchen has a lot of items, but it can be very simple to organize. Have separate, dedicated shelves or cupboards for your glasses, cups, plates, and bowls. You can even label the doors on the cupboards so that you don't have to show new friends where these items are. The same goes for herbs and spices, dry foods, canned goods, your pots and pans, cutlery and utensils, and cleaning products.

Chores and cleaning

When you get distracted easily or hyper-focus on a specific task, time might slip right by, resulting in a messy living space and dirty environment. This can get difficult when living with a partner, but even when you live by yourself, it can have a negative effect on your physical and mental health.

When a room is left without being cleaned regularly, the effort required to do so after a while is usually multiplied significantly. Thus, in order to make it easier and not be overwhelmed, break it up into daily tasks. One day, you can focus on cleaning the kitchen, and the next day, you can try to scrub the bathroom; the day following, you can sweep your house, and the day after you can mop. Perhaps you can try focusing on one room each day and cycling it around.

Cleaning smaller things like dishes and cups right after using them may seem tedious, or even just wiping down a table after eating might be an annoyance, but it will save you a night of washing a heap of dishes after a long day at work or eating at a table full of crumbs.

Schedule deep cleans for your home during the month. This will help you get into areas missed during basic and quick cleaning methods. During this time, you can even reorganize some areas that have started to get a bit cluttered or chaotic.

Build a Structure for Daily Life

So, now your home environment is controlled, making it so you can start your day off as smoothly as possible. This is not the only way to make your day go as you wish. Scheduling everything might seem bland, taking the fun out of everything, but that is not what scheduling is about, especially not for someone suffering from ADHD.

Structuring is not just about forming a schedule but also establishing routines that you can follow, making sure you do not miss appointments, special dates, and even keeping promises. Doing something regularly will form the connections in your brain needed to remember specific things, boosting your confidence and the confidence everyone has in you.

Routine

Setting up a basic routine to follow in the mornings is something that can be done easily, and it benefits every human on this planet. Perform your morning duties at the same time every morning as this will reassure you that you did not forget anything. It will also remove that feeling of unease when you leave for work wondering if you forgot something.

Set an alarm for waking up, and if you are a heavy sleeper, set more than one. Something that I personally benefit from is setting an alarm ten minutes before the time I need to get up and then snoozing it for those ten minutes. It has been proven that the feeling of having those extra few minutes to stay in bed gives us a much-needed morale boost in the early morning.

When establishing this routine, work on everything that benefits you personally that you might otherwise forget, like exercising, showering, brushing your teeth, or eating. Placing these tasks in a well-organized, timely routine will make sure you do not miss one or the other.

Preparation

The night before you can prepare certain things for the following morning, especially those of you who have trouble getting up, walking around kind of dazed the first few minutes of the morning. Set out your clothing, and make sure the items you need for work are in their designated spots, preferably somewhere you can see them when you leave, just in case you forget.

Scheduling

This is a very important part of any person's life, even more so when you have ADHD. Keeping a well-organized schedule for not just daily life but your work life as well will make a big difference in how people perceive you. Technology has made it so simple to keep a schedule, it's almost mind-boggling to see people running around without some sort of agenda in mind. If you prefer using the classic paper-and-pen method, there is nothing wrong with that either. A combination of both is where you might find the best result.

Time management is the key to keeping a schedule. Check how long it takes to perform your morning routine, and add those details to your schedule so you know when you are running behind or ahead. If you have a problem with always being late, take time every morning of each day and see which tasks take the longest, which ones can be removed or perhaps combined with others, and which ones might be the culprit for breaking your schedule.

When you are notified of a meeting taking place or an upcoming appointment, whether it is personal or work-related, add it to your schedule. This will help you avoid forgetting. There are many phone apps out there that make this easier, and there are even virtual assistants to utilize. Another method for remembering is placing sticky notes for important tasks or appointments somewhere you won't miss them.

A schedule is not just for work, however; it can help you keep your personal life in order, as well. Running errands can sometimes slip from your mind, and when you get home, you might realize you never stocked up your food cabinet or pantry.

Take a look at your weekly schedule to see when the best times are to go shopping for necessities, and keep a digital grocery list that you can update the moment you run out of something so you don't forget specific items.

Not every person is the same—not everyone will have the same schedule structure or method of keeping a routine. Find what works for you, whether you have ADHD or not. Forming a structure for each day will improve your quality of life tremendously. Try it for a month, and I guarantee you will see the difference.

Chapter 5:
Handling Hyperactivity, Stress, and Anxiety

Stress and anxiety are two emotional responses that pretty much every adult experiences at some point in their lives. Unfortunately, with adult ADHD, these manifestations of stress and anxiety can be a lot more detrimental. That is due in part to the problem of stress and anxiety being both a trigger for and a cause of ADHD symptoms.

Along with stress and anxiety, adult hyperactivity is incredibly misunderstood. Most articles and reports on adult ADHD talk about hyperactivity not being as severe in adults, or that it is one of the symptoms that can be "grown out of." While in some cases that is true, in most cases, hyperactivity simply manifests differently in adults than in children.

We decided to dedicate a whole chapter to hyperactivity, stress, and anxiety because they really do need a closer look. To help you succeed in managing ADHD symptoms as a whole, the more information you have in regard to these three topics, the better off you will be.

Another reason these three were singled out is because stress and anxiety are very common and over-medicated. It might be hard to believe, but with appropriate management, stress and anxiety can be overcome without any pharmaceutical intervention at all. If you go to a doctor with stress or anxiety, it is likely that they will prescribe you some kind of mild sedative or mood stabilizer to help you function day to day.

The same can be true of hyperactivity. A doctor will be more likely to prescribe a muscle relaxant or mild sedative to keep your body and mind calm. Medications can be helpful for the short term and help you get a certain control over the symptoms, but they aren't a fix or a cure. There is no guarantee the medications will help long term, plus they can come with a lot of side effects.

With adult ADHD, you'll probably be dealing with stress, anxiety, and hyperactivity for your whole life. As always, we ascribe to the belief that managing these symptoms holistically not only increases your functionality, but also makes you a stronger, better version of yourself.

Hyperactivity

Even though hyperactivity is noticeably lessened in adults, in most cases, it is still present and can be very difficult to deal with daily. More than that, hyperactivity can often be a distraction to those around you. Depending on how your hyperactivity presents, it might be an irritation for people who work near you. Your friends and coworkers might have a hard time keeping up with you.

You might not even know that certain actions or behaviors are a result of hyperactivity. You'll want to take a look at the next section to find out if you can identify your own hyperactivity. If you're already aware of it, great! However, sometimes it might manifest in multiple forms for you.

Self-awareness about how hyperactivity shows up in your adult life is going to be key in learning how to manage it. Children with ADHD usually show hyperactivity as constant motion. They want to run around in circles, climb every tree, jump off of rocks, roll down hills, skip, hop, and play all day long. Sometimes, there doesn't seem to be a space big enough to contain them.

Parents can find it difficult to keep up with that hyperactivity and don't necessarily know how to wear a child out enough to give themselves a break. It is important to make a distinction here between hyperactivity and children that don't get enough exercise. With the age of technology and the development of smartphones and tablets, it is more and more common for parents to hand their children a device to distract them and keep them "out of the way" or docile.

A lot of children who spend excessive time in front of screens aren't getting the ample amount of exercise or activity to help them express their natural energy levels. This can lead to trouble sleeping, acting out, and other behaviors that might appear to be hyperactivity. Children do tend to have higher energy levels than adults, but they still need appropriate ways to expend that energy or it gets pent up.

A child with ADHD never seems to be able to expend their energy. They can play at a playground all afternoon and still come home feeling wired and bouncing off the walls. They could ride their bike all around the neighborhood, and while the rest of their friends are exhausted, they'll want to play hopscotch or kick a soccer ball around.

This distinction may not seem important, but once ADHD symptoms evolve into adulthood symptoms, it makes a difference. When a child who was raised with excessive screen time and low exercise opportunities becomes an adult, they might not have healthy exercise habits and spend a lot of time watching television or playing video games. However, those are not signs of adult hyperactivity, just long-term habits.

When a child with ADHD grows into an adult, their hyperactivity is redirected. Most adults aren't climbing trees, running in circles, or rolling down hills. This is why hyperactivity is seen as 'lessening' in adults.

Maybe you would love to do all those crazy physical things just because your body constantly feels like a rocket ready for takeoff. Society imposes the inappropriateness of these actions in adults, which is another reason that adult hyperactivity seeps out in other ways.

What Hyperactivity Can Look Like

There are a lot of different ways that adults display hyperactivity. Most are subtle, but their presence can become problematic for themselves and for those around them.

Fidgeting is one of the most common ways that hyperactivity can manifest in adults. Fidgeting could be tapping your pencil or pen on your desk while you work, shifting the way you sit in your chair every few minutes, or tapping your fingers on your desk. Fidgeting is usually subtle. Depending on how severe your hyperactivity is, fidgeting can be a constant, or can be much more drawn out.

For example, tapping a pencil or tapping fingers can be an indication of more severe hyperactivity. It keeps the body in constant motion. This is true of leg bouncing, another common constant-motion fidgeting. Less severe hyperactivity might come as shifting your position in your chair every five to 10 minutes. This could happen at work or at home when you're on the couch. Between shifts, you are relatively still, which means your hyperactivity is sated for longer periods of time with small movements.

One adult who contributed to our research said that she and her husband end each day on the couch together. She will be reading a book and he will be playing a video game. Her fidgeting results in moving her legs around almost constantly. She will stretch them out over his lap, curl them up underneath her, push them against his legs, and put one leg on the back of the couch while the other is in his lap. As you can imagine, this becomes quite irritating for her husband when he is trying to concentrate or hold a game controller in his hands and lap.

While fidgeting is often subtle, it can cause problems for the people around you. Not everyone can concentrate when they hear the tapping of fingers or a pen. Your constant leg bouncing might noticeably shake the chair in the next cubicle over. If you shift your position in a work meeting every so often, it can become distracting to your coworkers.

Hyperactivity in adults can also show up as restlessness. This isn't the same as fidgeting, because often restlessness is felt internally. While it might compel you to get up and walk from the living room to the kitchen with no intention of getting a snack or a drink, the feeling itself is very internal.

Have you ever had restless leg syndrome? It is described as an almost painful feeling in the legs that feels like too much energy is built up. People with restless leg syndrome find they need to tense their leg muscles repeatedly, or stretch their legs, or even go for a walk to relieve the pain and sensations. Hyperactivity from adult ADHD can result in that restlessness throughout the entire body!

Sometimes restlessness can be limited to a specific region or body part. However, with more severe hyperactivity, it can spread everywhere. This internal restlessness can be very uncomfortable and almost painful. It can impede your ability to sleep and relax as well. It can become a distraction that prevents you from being able to get your work done or keeps you from focusing on anything other than what your body is feeling.

Restlessness can be quite uncomfortable, feeling like your muscles are buzzing under your skin, or like your skin is too tight. In some more unpleasant scenarios, it can even feel like bugs or something else is crawling on or under your skin. Even though restlessness is harder for someone else to see, your agitation and inability to concentrate can impact those around you.

Insomnia is another way that hyperactivity can show up in adults. Insomnia itself can present in many ways. Some forms make it very difficult to fall asleep. Other forms make it very difficult to stay asleep. Hyperactivity is attributed to not letting the brain "shut off." This means that your brain is always working, always thinking, always responding. Hence why a lot of hyperactivity can manifest in neurological ways.

If your brain can't relax and turn itself off, this can make it very difficult to get to sleep. Maybe you're lying in bed staring at your ceiling, and every time you try to drift off, some thought or worry jumps into your mind that brings you back to full alertness. With adult ADHD, that can be a result of hyperactivity. In other cases, you might not have any problem falling asleep. However, the moment a car drives by, or a street light flickers outside your window, you are awake and alert.

Sometimes fidgeting can even result in insomnia. If you are a fidgeter, there is a good chance that you toss and turn in your sleep. With a hyperactive mind, this tossing and turning can wake you up every single time! Some people with more severe hyperactivity have a combination of these manifestations that run roughshod all over their lives, and it can become difficult to manage.

Hyperactivity from adult ADHD isn't just limited to actions from the body. It can also come through in different behaviors, like babbling or talking very fast. Babbling is when you start talking and then just can't stop. One thought leads to another, which then sprouts into 500 different ideas or trains of thought, and you just keep talking, bouncing from one to the other. Babbling can be very difficult for other people to follow and can result in people not wanting to talk to you. Sometimes it is a nervous habit, but babbling can be caused by hyperactivity as well.

In some cases, people who babble also talk really fast. In other cases, you might talk fast without babbling. As soon as you get going, your speech patterns might increase and you feel like you are in a rush to get your words out. Unlike babbling, it doesn't result in an endless stream of ideas and thoughts, but talking fast has other drawbacks. Again, it is difficult to follow. It is also hard to enunciate when you talk fast, leaving room for misunderstandings and miscommunications.

Another communication pitfall that can be caused by hyperactivity is jumping around. Adults with ADHD can start a conversation about one topic and then have their thoughts pulled in a completely different direction. Then, they might try to circle back to the original topic. These conversations aren't linear and don't progress the same way other conversations do. For anyone else, they can be complicated and overwhelming. For the hyperactive mind, they seem normal.

In the same way that hyperactivity can cause someone to jump around in conversation, it can also lead to the mind losing its train of thought. If you are discussing a topic with someone else, and you are interrupted, or a really fancy car drives by, or your mind jumps ahead to a related topic, you could literally lose your train of thought mid-sentence. Have you ever had that moment where you were saying something, then stop talking and cannot for the life of you remember where your sentence was going?

Even if the distraction is as commonplace as the sound of birds singing when you are outside, the moment a hyperactive mind shifts to the distraction, it can erase everything that you were trying to say.

The best analogy that we have seen and used for this kind of hyperactivity is to compare the mind to a white board. Everyone's brain is a white board. Neurotypical people are able to organize their white board so that every time they receive new information or sensory input, they file that information into an open space on the white board. If the white board starts to fill up, they reorganize, begin writing smaller, and continue to accumulate information.

For someone with adult ADHD, the moment that you get new sensory input, a giant eraser sweeps across the white board and then a hot pink marker writes in giant, capital letters 'BIRD!' or a relative phrase to the distraction. All the information that was there before is gone, and conversations can become very broken.

Due to hyperactivity and the idea generation that comes with it, adults with ADHD can be very creative. They might be able to sit down and write 70,000 words of a novel in just three days. They might have sketchbooks full of sketches that just randomly popped into their heads. Their phones might be full of to-do lists for house renovation projects and business ideas. They have the potential to excel in the creative arts. However, other symptoms of ADHD can make it difficult for them to follow through with ideas or complete projects.

You might resonate with a few different types of hyperactivity that present in adults with ADHD. Maybe you've experienced all of them to varying degrees or severity. In reading about them, perhaps you've identified other types of hyperactivity that your body, mind, and behavior express regularly. The good news is that all hyperactivity can be managed and handled naturally; you just need to know what to do.

Managing Hyperactivity

Sometimes, managing hyperactivity comes down to lifestyle changes. Other times, it comes down to awareness and discipline. In regard to managing hyperactivity, the best way to get started is in self-discipline. By establishing discipline in your life, you will be able to manage excessive talking, babbling, or speed talking a lot more easily. You will also be able to channel your creative overflow of ideas and complete projects.

Chapter two went over a great deal of ideas and tips for establishing self-discipline and organization. Those don't often help with the hyperactivity of behavior and talking. Instead, you'll want to develop some self-disciplining habits that will prevent situations where you might babble or talk too fast.

Since ADHD is a lifelong condition, it is important to remember that these management techniques are not designed to eliminate hyperactivity. Your mind may always run in 10,00 directions at once with new ideas and concepts constantly blossoming. The goal is to rein in your behavior, body, and actions so that this hyperactivity doesn't affect your life in a negative way.

A good way to prevent yourself from babbling is to form the habit of taking a deep breath after each sentence. A deep breath would mean breathing in while mentally counting up to five, holding your breath for two seconds, and then breathing out again to the count of five. This exercise leaves space for others to respond to what you've said, and allows you to remain focused on the specific sentence that was spoken. It also clears the air so you can listen to what the people you are talking to respond with.

Sometimes one sentence isn't enough, so you might need to practice this deep breathing exercise after you express a complete thought or idea. Discipline yourself to take that breath so your conversations don't result in excess babble and other people can still contribute.

When it comes to preventing yourself from talking too fast, you can try getting in the habit of enunciating each syllable of a given word. By slowing down your speech pattern and focusing on the individual syllables, you'll be more understandable, but you also won't begin talking a million miles a minute. It takes practice and discipline to form this habit, but it will help you in communication.

Other ways to offset the results of hyperactivity include keeping the mind and body calm. There are a lot of different ways you can do this. Drinking a soothing, herbal tea like chamomile can help as it is a mild muscle relaxant. Maybe replace your morning coffee with a cup of chamomile tea with some honey.

Practicing deep breathing exercises can also help calm the body and mind. You can teach yourself deep breathing by following the pattern of breathing in for five seconds, holding your breath for five seconds, and then breathing out for 10 seconds. Repeating that breathing cycle for 20 full breaths helps sooth the body and mind. There are apps you can use right on your phone, YouTube videos, and podcasts that also offer breathing techniques for relaxation. If you practice deep breathing a few times a day, you'll notice a radical change in how hyperactive, fidgety, or restless you feel.

Taking several five-minute stretch breaks a day is a wonderful way to expel the energy that comes with hyperactivity. This is especially true if you work at a job that requires you to sit at a desk for most or all of your day. It is considered healthy to take a five-minute stretch break every hour for anyone working at a desk. For adults with ADHD, this is going to reduce fidgeting and restlessness as well.

You'll want to work on stretching your arms, legs, chest, hips/glutes, and neck primarily, as those are the body parts most negatively impacted by sitting at a desk long-term. However, it doesn't just have to be stretching. You could do a couple yoga poses or some squats and lunges as well.

While your employer might not let you get up and leave your desk to stretch, there are quite a few online tutorials for desk stretching routines that you can do right at your desk. Also, whenever you get a break, take a couple minutes to just walk around. On your lunch break, buy or bring lunch that you can eat while standing up. Bring snacks that meet the same criteria. Use that time to walk around your office, or even go outside for some fresh air and a walk.

Hyperactivity tells the body that it wants motion. You'll need to find ways to work different kinds of motion into your daily life to better manage hyperactivity. Even when you are at home or on your days off, if you've been sitting for more than an hour, get up and stretch or move around. Again, it takes discipline to develop these habits, but your body, mind, and the people around you will thank you for making the effort.

Another way to soothe the body and mind is to listen to calming music. Through music streaming services and YouTube, you can get access to a lot of very calming music. Regardless of what your taste in music is, if you try to listen to something instrumental and deeply relaxing a few times a day, your brainwaves can actually respond to that musical input. There is a song titled 'Weightless' by the artist Marconi Union that has been scientifically proven to relax the mind and body, reducing anxiety and stress by up to 65%! That is huge! Listening to similar music can have the same result, giving you more regulated activity and thought patterns (Curtin, 2017).

Stress and Anxiety

Stress, in this context, refers to an emotional or mental strain. It is a state of tension in the body as a result of that emotional or mental strain. Anxiety, for our purposes, is feelings of worry, concern, and nervousness. It can often be the result of an imminent event or situation.

If you've ever met someone who says they live "stress free" or they've never experienced anxiety, they are probably lying. Stress and anxiety are natural emotions and mental states that evolved as a response to certain stimuli. While humans don't necessarily need the same instincts that they needed when there was a threat of large predators or melting glaciers, those emotional responses do still mean something and serve a purpose to tell you something.

When you experience stress or anxiety, your body and mind are crying out to you and trying to get your attention. It is a good idea to start listening to what these emotions are trying to tell you.

As unfair as it sounds, adults with ADHD are more susceptible to experiencing stress and also having an anxiety disorder. Back in chapter one, we discussed how ADHD is often present with other behavioral health conditions. Mood disorders, which includes anxiety disorders, was present with a staggering 40% of adults with ADHD. Managing stress and anxiety caused by your ADHD is going to be your ticket to reducing their impact in your life and giving you a greater sense of normalcy.

A Vicious Circle

As previously mentioned, stress and anxiety make for complicated relationships with ADHD. When you are feeling stressed or anxious, they can aggravate your ADHD symptoms, which can lead to stress and anxiety.

When you are stressed out, it becomes impossible to filter out excess stimulation, sensation, and sensory input. This is why stress and anxiety can be so detrimental to the daily life of an adult with ADHD.

We should also distinguish between worry and anxiety. Yes, adults with ADHD are more likely to have an anxiety disorder, but not all adults with ADHD do. However, worry comes as a result of many of the ADHD symptoms. Worry is often directed at a specific idea, event, or concept. Anxiety is less focused. It manifests as an intense worry that does not have a target or a source.

Lack of time management and inability to manage finances can cause the mind a lot of worry, which in turn leads to more stress. Anxiety can be present, causing negative thoughts, mayhem, and lack of control without any discernible cause or root. Rather than worrying about paying bills, anxiety might come out as an overall frustration at the world.

ADHD symptoms, stress, and worrying anxiety are all interconnected. They create this merry-go-round of triggers that keep reacting to each other and getting worse as they feed off each other. It sounds horrifying! Please, don't become discouraged by that graphic description.

Between ADHD symptoms, stress from both sides, and the anxiety that comes with worry, ADHD can turn a good day into a bad day. An entire week can crumble into chaos, and the whole month might end up being less productive and downright depressing. There are clear genetic patterns that overlap between ADHD and anxiety and worry.

If all adults deal with stress and anxiety though, what sets stress and anxiety apart for adults with ADHD? Unfortunately, ADHD can actually lead to stress and anxiety running completely out of control. Unmanaged stress and anxiety can potentially lead to other health conditions like depression, Tourette's Syndrome, facial and muscular tics, chronic pain, and fibromyalgia.

There is a bright side though! Stress and worry are both triggered. Sometimes they are triggered specifically by ADHD symptoms, sometimes by something else. Any emotional response with a trigger can be managed or overcome. By bringing your stress and management under control, you free yourself up to have a more successful, ideal lifestyle.

Tips and Tricks for Handling Stress and Anxiety

The first step to managing stress and anxiety is to identify your triggers. A trigger could be as specific as the person working one cubicle over that always pops their gum, or as broad as social engagements with more than five people. When you know what your triggers are, you can help yourself manage stress and anxiety in those situations.

It is also important to note that triggers might be more intense if you aren't getting proper sleep, so while you are working towards managing stress and anxiety, you should also be developing healthy sleep habits.

Healthy sleep habits include:

- No caffeine after 12:00 p.m. It takes a long time to get out of the body, and will make it difficult to fall asleep.

- Set a specific schedule for sleep that involves going to bed and waking up at roughly the same time as often as possible.

- Cover the windows in your bedroom with heavy curtains and eliminate other exterior light sources.

- Stop using your phone, television, computer, or other screens at least half an hour before you are going to bed. The blue light stimulates your mind, making you think that it is daytime and feel less sleepy.

- Don't use your bed for anything but sleeping and sex. If you like to read before bed, do it on the couch or in a chair. You want to set the expectation for sleep when your head hits the pillow.

Adults with ADHD are especially prone to overstimulation with all the technology that is flying around. If you can limit your exposure to smart devices and computers, you'll cut down on overstimulation. When an ADHD mind becomes overstimulated, it quickly devolves into stress and anxiety. That will cut a large chunk of stress out of your life. Try giving yourself only a couple hours a day on the internet or social media sites. Maybe once a week, shut off all electronics and spend a whole 24 hours without internet or screens.

The skills and habits discussed in regard to managing hyperactivity can also be applied to stress management. That is particularly true of drinking soothing herbal teas, listening to calming music, and also practicing deep breathing exercises.

If you can, remove stressors and known triggers from your life. This might include certain people, places, events, or things that you know cause you stress and anxiety. Now, there will be situations where you won't be able to completely eliminate stressors, especially if they come from within your family or work. If you can work on setting firm boundaries between yourself and those people or situations, then you can shut out some of the stressful stimuli while still engaging with those people or situations.

Boundaries are a way of giving yourself control as well. If you can maintain control in the smaller aspects of your life, like at home, how you spend your free time, etc., then you won't feel as out of control in other areas of your life. Lack of control is a major contributor to stress and anxiety.

When you are stressed or anxious, don't go through it alone. Reach out to someone you trust and seek their support. Trying to handle it alone leads to brooding, repression, and uncontrolled emotional outbursts. This way, you have support, and additional perspectives to consider. Plus, talking about it is a good release, so you might not feel as stressed the next time it comes around.

If you have stress, anxiety, or worry about particular events or situations, it is often in regard to not knowing what to expect. So, do your research. Compile lists of facts so you can help put your mind at ease.

Drugs, including alcohol and nicotine, can exacerbate stress, anxiety, and worry. Stay away from drinking, drugs, and cigarettes to help you better manage your emotions and foster a calmer, more reasonable attitude.

You might need to make some changes to your lifestyle to better manage your stress and anxiety. However, in doing so, you can also alleviate your ADHD symptoms. It tends to be a win-win situation for you!

Chapter 6:
Holistic Treatment Options for Adult ADHD

ADHD is commonly treated with methylphenidate and/or amphetamines. These medications are effective in about 80 to 85% of people with ADHD. They also serve primarily to manage the symptoms by artificially correcting the neurological pathways in the brain. Medication certainly has its uses, but with any lifelong condition, medication can bring in problems of its own.

Most medications on the market these days have a host of side effects that only get worse when taken long term. Side effects can be as basic as mood swings, or as extreme as increasing your chance of developing diabetes. The longer you are on medications with side effects, the more likely you are to be affected by them.

Additionally, medications aren't a cure. They treat the symptoms, not the cause of the problem. In the instance of ADHD, they only mask or inhibit the symptoms, not treat them. When you're first prescribed a medication, it can take a while to get the dosage right, and a lot of times, things get worse before they get better. Once the sweet spot for dosage is found, it can rapidly change with fluctuations in weight, changes in diet, and emotional changes. Then it is right back to the beginning of fiddling with the dose to find the right balance.

More problems with medications are that a lot of them are recalled after only a few years; doses constantly need to be adjusted any time there is a change in your life, especially if it is a major event; and new medications are replacing old medications all the time. Some medications hit the shelf, and then a couple years later dangerous, long term side effects are discovered and the medication is immediately removed from circulation. It is hard to have any consistency when relying on prescription medication.

Since ADHD is a lifelong condition, to manage it with medication, you'd need to be on it your whole life. If you accidentally forgot to fill a prescription, or didn't pack any for a vacation you were going on, you might end up experiencing some rough days until you could get your medication again.

If you can manage your symptoms naturally and holistically, then you build a skill set that allows you to function with your symptoms rather than relying on a crutch to mask them. Your body and mind will be healthier long-term, and you won't be restricted by refills and the tumultuous nature of the ever changing medical field. It is true that managing your symptoms naturally can be more complicated than just taking a pill twice a day. You'll probably have to make some lifestyle changes to get the system right.

If we are speaking truthfully though, as someone with a neurological disorder, lifestyle changes will be necessary in order for you to succeed and excel in the areas you want to.

Supplements for Adult ADHD

Some people might see supplements as just a replacement for medications. It is true, supplements often come in capsule form and have a dosage structure like medications. Most of the supplements that are used for treating ADHD can also be consumed through food and diet though.

Furthermore, supplements are made of natural ingredients. There will never be a recall on Vitamin C for being unsafe because it is a vitamin that the body needs to survive. Vitamins, minerals, and supplements tend to be good for the body, but that doesn't mean they are without risk. The body requires a certain balance, and anything that is consumed in excess can become problematic.

Before you decide to take any of these supplements, consult your doctor or primary care physician, especially if you are on any medication. You don't want to have conflicting treatments. Most supplement bottles come with warnings about pregnancy, breastfeeding, and other health conditions, but if you have a preexisting condition or are pregnant, nursing, or trying to become pregnant, clear with a qualified professional that the supplement won't cause problems.

Doses for vitamins and minerals tend to be pretty straight forward. They are usually a "one size fits all" kind of deal, but you can also discuss with a qualified healthcare provider what the best course of treatment is with these supplements.

Each supplement and vitamin that is covered in this section will reference foods that the vitamin or mineral can be obtained through. However, more on diet and nutrition will be elaborated in a later section.

So, supplements are great because they are easy to use, not a lot of changes are rolled out in regard to their safety or composition, and your body needs most of them to function naturally anyway. Using supplements can improve your overall health as well as help with ADHD symptoms.

Supplements are growing in popularity. There are entire stores that just sell supplements. A lot of grocery stores carry them now too. Natural markets are also a good place to find supplements. You can even buy them online, although we'd urge you to research the company before making an online purchase to ensure the purity of the product.

Omega-3s

Omega-3s are fatty acids that are most commonly found in cold-water fish. Sardines and salmon are known to be rich in omega-3s. These omega-3s are known to help with cognitive skills, behavior, and focus in people with ADHD.

Studies have indicated that omega-3s that are taken in doses optimized for ADHD are 40% as effective as ADHD prescription medications (ADHD Editorial Board, 2020). While that might seem like a low percent, when it is combined with other natural treatments, it can make a huge difference.

Zinc

Another mineral that the body needs, zinc can be harmful in large doses. Definitely confirm the dosage with a healthcare provider to avoid entering those harmful levels.

For ADHD, zinc has been known to reduce hyperactivity and can also help with impulsivity. Furthermore, a zinc deficiency can lead to inattention. Zinc is a great mineral to work against the three major symptoms of ADHD.

While it is fairly easy to come across zinc in supplement form, there are plenty of foods that contain zinc as well. Oysters are the highest natural source of zinc in the human diet. However, not everyone likes oysters or can get their hands on them easily. Red meat and poultry are a natural source of zinc, as are beans, nuts, crab, lobster, whole grains, and dairy products.

Iron

There is some discussion in the medical community that low iron levels in the body can actually aggravate ADHD symptoms. Having regulated iron levels can improve behavior related to ADHD symptoms.

There are plenty of natural sources of iron, including lean beef, chicken, turkey, and oysters. There are also some non-meat-based sources as well, including beans and lentils, baked potatoes, cashews, dark leafy greens, whole grain bread, and tofu. Your body will absorb more iron through meat sources, but you can also get other needed vitamins through the vegetable sources, like Vitamin C.

Magnesium

Magnesium is a natural calming agent. It is considered beneficial for hyperactivity and can help to calm the mind and the brain. It is another vital mineral for the body and deficiencies can lead to more than just problems with ADHD symptoms.

You can get magnesium through a lot of different food sources. There are several fish options, such as halibut, Atlantic mackerel, and salmon. You can also get magnesium through vegetables like spinach, swiss chard, and potatoes with skins.

Vitamin D

Vitamin D is a crucial vitamin for a lot of different reasons. A study showed that children with ADHD had lower levels of Vitamin D than children without ADHD. It was also found that mothers with low Vitamin D while pregnant were more likely to have children with ADHD (Newmark, 2020).

Vitamin D is most easily absorbed through the eyes with exposure to sunlight. This poses other problems as there are some regions, such as New England in the United States, and further north, where the latitude doesn't allow for enough annual sun for those who are Vitamin D deficient to absorb enough Vitamin D year round.

Another important benefit of Vitamin D is that it helps to combat depression, which is a common health concern that coincides with ADHD symptoms.

The best natural source of Vitamin D is the sun. Few foods actually contain Vitamin D. Small amounts exist in beef liver, egg yolks, and cheese. Also, fatty fish skins, like from mackerel, tuna, or salmon, have some Vitamin D.

Vitamin C

Another necessary vitamin and antioxidant, Vitamin C is known to the dopamine neurotransmitter in the brain. Dopamine is a brain hormone that helps your brain communicate with the rest of your body. It is a pleasure hormone, and when it isn't being regulated, it can lead to depression and mood disorders.

Doctors do not recommend taking Vitamin C within an hour of taking prescribed ADHD medication.

Both fruits and vegetables are great sources of Vitamin C. Citrus fruit like oranges and grapefruits are a good source. Other fruits include kiwi, cantaloupe, pineapple, and berries (strawberries, blueberries, cranberries, and raspberries). Vegetables that have Vitamin C include green and red peppers, sweet and white potatoes, tomatoes, winter squash, spinach, and broccoli.

Ginkgo Biloba

Ginkgo biloba is the only supplement on our list that isn't a necessary vitamin, mineral, or antioxidant for the body. However, it is an herbal supplement that has been used in herbal remedies and natural medicines for thousands of years. One of ginkgo's claims is that it can improve cognitive function. In a study done on children with ADHD, those that took a stimulant with added ginkgo showed a 35% improvement in rate in terms of attention and memory over the children that were on the stimulant and the placebo (Newmark, 2020).

This supplement is pretty easy to get your hands on and has actually been suggested for use in helping with memory loss and degenerative memory disorders. Short-term memory can also be a problem for adults with ADHD. It is generally safe, but as an herb that isn't necessary to the body, it is a good idea to discuss using it with a qualified health care professional.

Nutrition and Diet

It is no secret that diet and nutrition are major components to overall physical and mental health. The impact of diet and nutrition on ADHD specifically is a bit controversial; however, we've already discussed a plethora of great foods that are healthy for you and also provide you with minerals, vitamins, and antioxidants that can help with ADHD symptoms. Making those foods part of your regular diet is recommended, as long as you are considering the health factors for eating them in moderation.

There is some research that argues foods with excessive sugar, coloring and dyes, and additives can contribute to ADHD or exacerbate the symptoms. The data to back up this claim isn't conclusive enough to be convincing. There are other ways that diet and nutrition impact the body and mind though.

Adults with ADHD are prone to poor nutrition in the form of eating high-carb and high-sugar foods, but not drinking enough fluids. More often than not, this comes down to improper planning. Some of the symptoms of ADHD can lead to forgetfulness and bad time management, leading to missed mealtimes. When a mealtime is missed, they will make up for it with unhealthy snacks to power through their day.

Another common problem that adults with ADHD end up facing with nutrition is caffeine. A lot of adults with ADHD will self-medicate with caffeine to deal with bad sleep schedules. They might also use caffeine to self-medicate rather than take stimulant medication. While it is true that caffeine can mimic some of the effects of ADHD prescription medications, it isn't as potent and ends up causing other problems in the body and with natural sleep patterns.

When you first start reorganizing your diet and nutrition to better aid in your ADHD treatment, begin with taking an inventory of what you eat any given day. Make a list each day for a week of everything that you eat and drink. You might also want to write down the foods you keep in your home and what is commonly on your grocery shopping list. You could also write down a list of all your favorite places to eat out.

Using those lists, you are going to want to begin cutting out high-fat, high-sugar, and high-carbohydrate foods, especially the snacky foods. You don't have to make a huge change in one big swoop either. Maybe you'll start cutting out sugary foods, then move onto the carbohydrate-heavy snacks. Take it slow; otherwise your body might feel strange as it adjusts to a different diet, and you could get frustrated and give up altogether.

Consider healthy snack alternatives. Carry pre-proportioned, protein-rich, healthy snacks with you, such as natural peanut butter carrot sticks, nuts and seeds, or cheese sticks. If you have a real sweet tooth, replace sugary snacks with some yummy fruits. Adhere to portion-controlled standards, but try supplementing those sugar cravings with some cherries, strawberries, or mango instead.

Overall, eating raw, clean, whole foods is better than eating processed, preservative-heavy foods. Raw, clean, whole foods would be like vegetables, fruits, nuts, lean, grass fed meats, eggs, etc. While the link between chemicals in foods and ADHD isn't solid, a lot of those heavily processed foods, like snack foods, boxed meals, frozen dinners, pasta, crackers, etc., do have preservatives and chemicals that can be unhealthy for the body overall.

Sticking to a clean diet gives your body the vitamins, minerals, and antioxidants that it needs. You'll also have more control over eating the foods that have the vitamins, minerals, and antioxidants that help your ADHD symptoms. That way, you won't have to rely on supplements to balance the body's function.

Improving overall health and wellness with diet can contribute to better moods and improved mental health. In this case, you are eliminating other potential conflicts with ADHD that could be major setbacks for yourself. It is always important to take care of your body, and taking care of your body can drastically alter the severity of your ADHD symptoms.

Another recommendation is to cut caffeine out of your diet. If you feel like you need a kind of jolt in the morning, consider rooibos tea or peppermint tea. Both are herbal with no caffeine, but they also offer a natural energy boost. A little honey and a splash of milk can make them very delicious and give you a natural sweetener to help those sugar cravings.

Another tea option is green tea. While green tea does have low levels of caffeine, it is also one of the superfoods and has a strong connection to brain function. There is no direct correlation between green tea and ADHD, but it is known to improve brain function overall, which can help with ADHD symptoms.

It can be complicated and difficult to rearrange your diet so that you reach optimal nutrition. If you don't know how to cook or aren't comfortable cooking, there are plenty of meals and snacks that you can transition to that don't require cooking. However, eating raw, clean, and whole foods does require more preparation than the premade, frozen, or snack-like foods. You might want to look into taking a cooking class or getting a lesson from someone you know who cooks.

Diet is probably one of the greatest struggles for a lot of people. Unhealthy food is so convenient and readily available. It is fast, hassle free, and often less expensive. Unfortunately, you aren't doing yourself or your ADHD any favors if you default to unhealthy foods. Food and changing your diet is one of the hardest commitments for people to stick to, even neurotypical adults.

Try shopping at a natural food market where access to common, unhealthy snacks isn't as easy. If you have a farmer's market nearby, go shopping there, as all the food is raw, clean, and whole. Changing your diet is the same as building other healthy habits to manage your ADHD symptoms.

Exercise

Just like with diet and nutrition, exercise is vital to overall health and wellness. With ADHD, exercise is a little more relevant though. Being active is one of the greatest ways to help a hyperactive mind. Not only does your body get to expend energy, but it can actually wear your mind out to the point where you can focus better and feel more productive.

Exercise not only aids the body, but the mind as well. When you exercise, your brain produces endorphins which contribute to improved mood overall. Other hormones that are increased in the brain with exercise are dopamine and serotonin, which contribute to focus and attention.

Being active can be difficult though. Between a full-time job, a house, and a family, finding the time to be active or have a regular exercise routine can get complicated. Fortunately, there are a few options for ADHD that are actually very easy to work into your busy schedule.

Walking is a gentle form of exercise that you can do virtually anywhere, and you don't need to be an avid exerciser to manage walking. To decrease hyperactivity, improve attention, reduce impulsivity, and manage other ADHD symptoms, a 30-minute walk four times a week will help. That's it! You don't even need to walk every single day, although you can if you want and have the time.

Aerobic exercise, such as yoga, can also relieve ADHD symptoms. Classes and routines can be as short as 30 or 45 minutes to be effective on ADHD symptoms. While classes can get expensive and time consuming, there are a lot of phone applications, YouTube videos, online services to get yoga classes and quick workout routines on the go that you can do in your own home. It cuts out the travel and often the financial aspects, and you can do them whenever you find the time.

Skill-based exercises are probably the most beneficial to adult ADHD. A skill-based exercise is one that focuses on a skill set, such as martial arts or belly dancing. This kind of exercise is often one you need to learn in a class with an instructor, but is highly recommended if you have the time and means.

Now, not everyone is accustomed to regular exercise. If you aren't, then it can be hard to get into the habit or routine. Just like with diet, adding exercise into your life is a commitment that you'll need to make in order to improve your overall functionality.

Start slow with a 10-minute walk every day, building up to that 30-minute walk four times a day. The good thing about exercise is that it doesn't have to be rigorous, designed to build muscle tone, or intense. You don't need to run out and get a gym membership and start lifting weights or running on the treadmill.—although, if that is your goal for exercise, get right into it.

You can decide how to best work exercise into your schedule, and what you want to gain from exercising. If you just want to help manage your ADHD symptoms, you don't need anything extreme. However if you also want to get in shape, improve your body health, or maybe train to run a marathon, then choose your exercise plan based on your goals. Walking 30 minutes four times a week isn't going to leave you toned and fit.

Another form of exercise, which is hobby based and isn't considered working out, is gardening. If you have an interest in gardening, it can be incredibly beneficial for your ADHD symptoms. Gardening is task and skill oriented. You use a lot of different muscles in the body for weeding, planting, pruning, harvesting (if you grow veggies or fruits), etc.

Depending on how big of a garden you have, it can be quite time consuming, but if you stick to it, you'll be left with a sense of productivity and be rewarded when the flowers begin to bloom. Several adults with ADHD have discussed how gardening can help recharge them after a rough day or week, while also helping them exercise. Being outside, being active, and being in nature is incredibly refreshing and rejuvenating. If you have the space, consider gardening an alternative to conventional exercise.

So, work on adding exercise into your weekly routine. Ideally you'll be able to exercise a little every day. Outside exercise is great because you also get fresh air.

Sleep and Relaxation

Lack of sleep, unhealthy sleep, and interrupted sleep are major contributors to stress and ADHD episodes. As strange as it sounds, you actually have to build healthy sleep habits for yourself and teach yourself how to relax in order for your mind and body to recharge. Even with hyperactivity, your body and mind need time to reboot. Think of your brain as a very sophisticated computer. Even computers need to be shut down and rebooted in order to optimize their function.

That catch-22 is that ADHD can make it really difficult to sleep or relax. Have you ever felt like every time you try to relax, 10 things suddenly pop up that need your attention? Or maybe you keep telling yourself "after I wash the dishes, I'll sit down," and then just keep adding to your to-do list? These are byproducts of hyperactivity and an inability to focus.

Sure, you might feel productive getting some extra chores done, but it is a mental distraction from your goal to relax. Say you want to sit down and read for a little while. As soon as you open your book, your mind might remind you that the laundry needs to be switched to the dryer, or you haven't checked the mail today.

You might get through a paragraph or two, and then maybe you'll start thinking about the name of the main character in your novel. Suddenly, that name is very interesting, so you put your book down and pull out your computer. You research the origins of the name, its meaning, popularity, and anything else you can find about that name.

These kinds of distractions are rather common for an ADHD mind when trying to relax. There are some methods you can implement to help you relax more effectively, giving your body and mind the rest they need.

There are several relaxants that you can drink or consume in one way or another before you sit down to read or decide to watch a movie. Chamomile tea, catmint tea, and magnesium drink powder can be drunk before and/or during your relaxation period. They help to soothe the body and mind to a point where you can settle down and recharge.

Burning incense or diffusing essential oils is another option for creating a relaxing atmosphere. Lavender is an incredibly soothing and relaxing herb. If you have lavender essential oil, diluting a couple drops in a four ounce spray bottle makes a relaxing spray. Spritz it on your pillow on your bed, rub it on the bottom of your feet, or dab the spray on your temples. Other herbs that can be relaxing are sage, ginger, and tulsi basil.

Music is another great method for slowing your mind and body down. There are a lot of different music options that are scientifically proven to alter your brainwaves to help you relax.

Practice relaxing with any of the discussed methods and see what works best for you. What do you like to do to relax? Do you read, write, knit, game, draw, or scroll through social media? Whatever you like to do to relax, pair it with one of these relaxation methods to make the most of it.

In chapter three, healthy sleep habits were covered in regard to hyperactivity. Healthy sleep and relaxation are going to benefit all your ADHD symptoms. You can use these concepts and ideas interchangeably for relaxing and sleeping.

Creating Healthy Thought Patterns

A lot of the trouble around ADHD symptoms is how self-critical adults with ADHD can be. Sometimes this is a result of external influences from comments or statements they hear from other people. Other times it is just a case of being their own worst enemy. Whatever the reason, creating healthy thought patterns is a good way to combat yourself.

The brain, including emotions and thought patterns, follows the same pathways over and over. What that means is that if you react negatively to someone calling you short, your brain forms a habit to react negatively any time someone calls you short. However, you can train your brain to respond differently with thoughts and emotions.

This can be difficult to do on your own. You might find that therapy, specifically cognitive therapy and behavioral therapy, will help you establish healthier thought patterns. Therapy is a wonderful resource that pretty much everyone can benefit from at some point in their life. There are a lot of stigmas and misconceptions around therapy; however, it is natural and holistic and can help a lot.

If you choose the route of therapy, you'll want to look for a therapist who has been trained in cognitive and/or behavioral therapy. You'll also want to look for therapists who have experience working with adults with ADHD. This is how you make the most of your therapy experience. It is worth noting that you could find a therapist who meets all those prerequisites, but that you don't feel entirely comfortable with.

Finding a therapist is like picking a car. Sometimes you need to test drive a few of them before you find the one you are looking for. Don't think that if your first

105

attempt doesn't go well that therapy can't help you. You just need to find the right fit for you.

Changing your thought patterns and creating healthier thoughts and emotional responses can be accomplished on your own without therapy. This is more difficult, can take a lot of work, and can be particularly hard for people with ADHD. The ADHD mind has more difficulty forming patterns and won't be as disciplined as if someone was helping them along, like a therapist.

That being said, a few options for improving thought patterns include using daily affirmations. Affirmations are quite universal and stem from the idea that everyone makes their own reality. An affirmation could be "today I will eat a healthy lunch." They can also be much more general and be something like "today I will not get angry." By telling yourself you will think or behave a certain way, you make it so. A lot of people who use affirmations like to repeat them to themselves throughout the day, or write them on a sticky note and keep it where they can see it throughout the day as a reminder.

After a while, the idea is that your mind begins to default to the healthier thought pattern that you are creating with affirmations.

You can use certain applications to help you change your thought patterns. There are apps for meditation, deep breathing, and similar techniques that also assist in creating different thought patterns.

If you can change the way you think about yourself, you can change the way other people think about you.

Healthy thought patterns improve mood, help you manage your emotions, and help alter your behavioural patterns, and thus help manage your ADHD symptoms.

Chapter 7:
Self-Help Options for Adult ADHD

Along with the holistic treatment options, there are some self-help or self-care options that you can implement to help manage ADHD symptoms. Self-care isn't necessarily about targeting your ADHD symptoms for treatment, but it can be effective in reducing symptoms and helping you manage them.

Self-help is the concept of improving yourself emotionally, economically, or intellectually. There are libraries of books on self-help and how to change the way you think, feel, and view life. By partaking in generalized self-help programs or regimes, you can expand on the skill sets that are required to be more self-disciplined and more structured. In turn, you can use those skills to better manage your adult ADHD.

Self-care is very similar to self-help that it is about improvement. However, self-care is related more to functionality of the body and mind that is within your control. Rather than trying to change yourself, self-care is meant to increase the overall health and wellness for your body, mind, and spirit.

In a lot of modern societies, there is an emphasis on ignoring self-care. We are told from a young age that we should focus on schoolwork, building a career, making money, raising a family, etc. While all those aspects contribute to a well-oiled society, they remove any sense of individuality. Children in school are limited to a generalized academic program that doesn't really let them explore or expand on hobbies. Adults working full time often go for the job that will pay their bills, not make them happy.

As a result, any kind of self-care is associated with 'selfishness' or as a 'luxury.' Society runs smoothly, but we are just cogs in the machine. The notion of self-care gives each individual a sense of themselves back. It encourages them to explore hobbies, passions, and take care of their own basic needs so that they can be better at work, be more responsive to their family, etc.

When it comes to ADHD, self-care is important because the stress and anxiety that can trigger and/or be a result of symptoms can be debilitating. The emphasis on self-care is to reduce stress and anxiety as well as feed your emotional and mental health. As a neurological disorder, ADHD is directly related to mental health.

The self-help and self-care methods that are elaborated on in this chapter are going to focus on reducing stress and anxiety, but also promote cognitive function and mental strength. Self-help and self-care are very wide fields and there are probably other options that you know of, or will learn of, that you decide you like and want to use.

Meditation

Meditation has been used for thousands of years for a variety of different reasons. It has been a main component of a lot of spiritual practices and rituals, and has been used in therapy, hypnosis, and in the pursuit of greater knowledge and understanding.

While meditation can be transformative, it isn't necessarily about becoming a different person, changing the way you think, or even about controlling your thoughts. More accurately, it is about not letting your thoughts control you. This is important for adults with ADHD.

One of the great benefits of meditation is that it is free, easy to practice on your own, and available to everyone. There are a lot of different kinds of meditations. Guided meditation is when you use a recording or have an in person guide to speak to you, walking you through the steps of a specific meditation with their words.

Another form of meditation is group meditation. This is usually a guided meditation; however, you are with a whole group of people that are participating in the same guided meditation. This type of meditation is great for beginners and gives you a resource of other meditators to discuss your experiences with and learn from.

You can meditate on your own as well, without the guiding aid of a voice. There are fantastic resources that can help you learn the basics of lying-down meditation, standing meditation, and even walking meditation. Each position approaches the concept slightly differently.

Sitting meditation is probably one of the most commonly recognized forms of meditation. The classic image of a person sitting cross legged with their spine straight and their palms turned up on their knees is what is usually imagined when someone hears 'meditation' or "sitting meditation." This posture is also referred to as Zen meditation.

Deep breathing meditation is another common style of meditation that is recognized and used. There are so many possibilities that you can play around with what kind of meditation you like most. You might decide to dabble in a lot of the methods before picking a favorite, or use a few of them based on what you are feeling.

The benefits of meditation for ADHD include calmness, relaxation, clearer thoughts, and an improvement in emotional and overall health. Additionally, the benefits of meditation don't only last for the duration of your session. Even after the meditation ends, you can carry that calmness and clarity through the rest of your day. That added benefit is particularly beneficial to adults with ADHD.

Meditation can improve your focus. Guided meditations are a fantastic way to exercise your imagination while also keeping your focus. The words you listen to keep you on track, but your imagination still conjures the imagery to accompany the words. This is another reason that guided meditation is great for beginners in meditation, regardless of if they have ADHD or not.

If you are a beginner to meditation, it can be difficult to build the necessary focus to benefit from meditation. There is a difference between meditating and sitting comfortably in a dimly lit room with your eyes closed, breathing deeply and letting your thoughts flow. Meditation does take practice, focus, and repetition. The ADHD mind can struggle to maintain that focus and clarity, especially in the beginning.

To help build up your meditation skills, you should start small. Dedicate three to five minutes a day to meditating. A smaller commitment is much easier to stick to and gives your mind room to practice meditation skills without taking on too much. After a week of successful three- to five-minute meditations, add another five minutes, or bump yourself up to 10 minutes.

Complete another week of successful 10-minute meditations before moving onto 15 minutes, and so forth. You can cap yourself off at some point, like 20, 30, or 45 minutes, or keep practicing with incremental increases for as long as you want. The longer you can meditate for, the greater the increase in focus you will develop.

You can perform meditations for specific goals or to seek answers to questions as well. This kind of meditation is done by accessing the subconscious mind for clarity on topics that you might not be able to think about clearly from a conscious mind standpoint.

As far as meditation and ADHD symptoms go, the benefits are incredibly obvious. Meditation can help temper hyperactivity and impulsivity with the calming and relaxation it fosters. It can help enhance focus and clarity of thought for the wandering mind that gets distracted and can't complete tasks. Meditation can create a sense of peace, allowing you to accept yourself and the circumstances of your life, including having adult ADHD. Furthermore, meditation can actually aid in the treatment of mood disorders, especially depression. It has been recommended and used with patients that are recovering from substance abuse and different aspects of meditation are used in various forms of cognitive and behavioral therapy.

Since meditation is meant to be peaceful and reflective, it is great for a hyperactive mind because it essentially forces you to remove all external distractions for the duration of your meditation. That way, you have a better chance of learning how to manage your internal distractions (thoughts, emotions, anxiety, etc.).

Scientifically speaking, meditation can quite literally alter your brainwaves, which is why the effects can last throughout the whole day. The most commonly used brainwaves are delta, theta, alpha, beta, and gamma.

Delta brainwaves are the slowest and accompany a dreamless sleep. They are the healing and regeneration waves. Theta waves are the second slowest, occurring when dreaming, relaxing, or daydreaming. They coincide with a deep focus, leading to vivid imagery. Beta waves and alpha waves are the brainwaves that your mind experiences most frequently when awake.

Alpha waves are the next fastest, and are associated with being awake and alert, yet calm. Imagine when you first wake up in the morning and are just getting going.

That is the alpha state. Beta are the most common brainwaves and are the second fastest. With beta waves you are awake, alert, active and busy. You've had your morning coffee and are at work getting things done. Gamma waves are the absolute fastest and indicate higher brain function, like higher consciousness, problem solving, and perception.

When you meditate, the goal is to dip your mind intentionally into the theta wave range. Not only is it the range associated with deep focus, but that "waking dream" state allows you access to your subconscious thoughts and reactions. Theta waves are slower, which help to counteract hyperactivity in the mind.

Meditation isn't a cure for ADHD symptoms by any means, but by altering your brainwave patterns and developing that focus and calmness, you can make a huge difference in your everyday functionality.

Teaching yourself how to meditate is quite easy. You can use phone apps, YouTube videos, podcasts, and other online, free resources to learn and practice meditation. You can also pay for an instructor to guide you or find a meditation group to join for the added support. Getting in the habit of meditating every day is highly beneficial for ADHD and mental and emotional health in general.

Massage, and Bodywork

Some self-care methods require the assistance of a professional. It is still considered self-care because you are putting the time and finances into getting the work done on yourself. There are also some things you can't really do for yourself. Massage, as an example, is really hard to perform on yourself. You can't really give yourself a full body massage, even if you are a massage therapist.

Bodywork in general has a lot of health benefits that are both physical and mental. Massage is one of the most commonly practiced and used forms of bodywork; however, it is not the only kind out there. For our purposes, 'bodywork' is going to refer to a practice in which a qualified professional touches and otherwise manipulates your body in some way.

A few well-known forms of bodywork include massage, reflexology, and acupuncture. Each of these categories has several different subcategories that have additional techniques and methods. Massage has a whole slew of different kinds, such as sports massage, lymphatic massage, shiatsu, lomi lomi, hot stone massage, and many more. Reflexology even has different techniques that provide various benefits.

The focus here is on the benefits of massage in a general way. We aren't going to go into the specifics of the different styles and how they differ or what additional benefits they carry. If you are interested in learning more, we encourage you to do so and find what appeals most to you.

As with a therapist, finding a massage practitioner to treat you can be a process. You want to find someone that you feel comfortable with, who will respect the boundaries you set, and who understands why you are seeking this form of treatment. Massage professionals are well educated, and you can find those in niches for mental health or neurological disorders.

Massage

Massage is essentially a practice in which a trained professional manipulates the muscles, soft tissues, tendons, and ligaments of a body for relaxation and medical purposes. There is some joint manipulation as well, but it isn't as intense or focused as chiropractic therapy.

Massage is an ancient form of healing, and in some countries it is so valued as part of healthcare that massage therapists are paid almost as much as doctors. It is both maintenance and preventative therapy, meaning it helps at the time you get a massage and also contributes to the prevention of injury and illness down the road.

The most well-known benefits of massage include:

- Reduction in muscular tension

- Relaxation

- Better blood circulation

- Increase in lymph movement

- Decrease in stress hormones

- Better skin and skin tone

- Increased flexibility and joint mobility

- Better soft tissue injury recovery

- Better mental alertness

- Improvements with depression and anxiety

For anyone with adult ADHD, relaxation, reduced stress, reduced depression and anxiety, and more mental alertness are all great qualities and benefits from massage. Reducing tension in the body can also have a profoundly stress-reducing effect.

Another great benefit of massage for ADHD symptoms is that while getting a massage, you can enter a deeply meditative state, leading to focus and clarity of thought. After a massage, a lot of people experience what is called "massage brain" where they are so relaxed and on such an endorphin high they can't form a complete thought. This can really help slow a hyperactive mind down for a break and a recharge.

Since massage is physical, it can also release built-up energy and tension in the muscles and limbs. This can be an aid to the fidgeting and restlessness than can build up in the body. Over time, that energy can build up again, but by getting it regularly released from massage, your body will feel less discomfort from day to day. Since massage works the soft tissues too, having your fascia and connective tissues worked is another way to reduce restlessness by improving mobility. You feel less tight in your skin.

There is a specialized type of massage called neuromuscular massage. This form of massage is used to reprogram the muscles and their connection to the nervous system. While it won't fix a neurological disorder, reprogramming nerves, even at a muscular level, can help ease some of the neurological discrepancies.

Another form of massage is called cranial sacral massage. One of its purposes is to increase the flow of cerebrospinal fluid which can contribute to better brain function and improved cognitive function.

There are plenty of different kinds of massage that can be beneficial to ADHD. Even your basic, full body Swedish massage has its benefits. Plus, it feels good and you get to relax while someone else does the work. Massage can get pricey and not everyone can afford to pay for it regularly, but if you can get a massage every four to six weeks, you'll see a change in how your body handles your ADHD symptoms.

Mindfulness

Similar in many ways to meditation, mindfulness can actually be combined with meditation. On its own, mindfulness is the practice of being present, being aware of the moment around you, and interacting with your five senses in each and every moment. It is a great way to develop focus and awareness, and to reduce stress and anxiety.

A lot of anxiety comes from worry, which comes from thinking about the future, future events, and unknowns of the future. By practicing mindfulness, you focus on the now, the present, and that anxious future doesn't exist or bother you.

Mindfulness can help with follow-through. By remaining present in a specific task, you limit distracting thoughts and stimuli that draw your attention away. By including all five senses (sight, hearing, feeling, tasting, and smelling) in each experience that you have, you can let your mind shift between sensations, giving it some freedom to explore without being drawn away from the task.

You can practice mindfulness by incorporating it into your meditations, using guided mindfulness practices, or coming up with your own. You can also practice mindfulness with everything you do. Eating can become a mindful experience, removing any stimuli except the food in front of you. As you eat, go slowly and savor every single bite, smell, and flavor.

Mindfulness can be as easy as deep breathing exercises where you focus on your breaths. Counting exercises are also a mindful practice where you count your breaths, or your steps, or some other action you perform while remaining focused on it. Although, you don't have to limit mindfulness to such a narrow range of activity either.

If you struggle to complete chores or get easily distracted, turn washing dishes or folding laundry into a mindfulness exercise. Without the constant need to look ahead, your mind and body slow down to focus. These are great skills to build that will then help you manage your other ADHD symptoms.

Most people live their lives rushing from one activity or task to the next. They are constantly thinking ahead to what needs to get done and what they have to do in a day. This mentality is what creates anxiety and stress. Constantly looking ahead means you will be pressured to rush through everything so you can finish what you've set for yourself in a given day. More than that, if you are constantly looking ahead, you can miss some really incredible experiences right in front of you.

It doesn't take a hyperactive mind to feel crazy, disorganized, and like you are constantly running all over the place. Of course, a hyperactive mind doesn't help, and combined with other ADHD symptoms can lead to other complications. So, mindfulness can be used as a tool to settle yourself down and focus on the here and now. That way, you won't miss any of the small moments, like how the flowers smell every time you step through your front door, or the way your kids smile at you every time you make them a snack.

When you practice mindfulness, it can also lead to more rational thought. Since you slow yourself down, you can think about what you are doing. Thus, the impulsivity of adult ADHD can be managed and controlled much easier. Impulse buying is one of those things that can drain your bank account or prevent you from having money for bills. With ADHD, your mind doesn't always pause to consider the ramifications. Instead, you leap headlong into a purchase for something you can't afford or might not even need.

The more you incorporate mindfulness practices into your daily tasks, the more you develop mindful thought processes and patterns. So, after working at it for a while, when you go to reach for your wallet to buy that brand new smart TV even though you have a perfectly functional TV at home that hardly gets used, your mindfulness will kick in and make you pause and listen to your rational thoughts.

It isn't a perfect method. Mindfulness is more about experiencing something rather than doing it. Yet, that mentality does help with impulsivity.

Start small, maybe with some mindful breathing techniques. There are apps, YouTube videos, podcasts, and books that can help you learn the basics of mindfulness and give you some helpful breathing techniques. Combining mindfulness and meditation can save you a little time and help you organize your schedule better.

Like meditation, you'll have to practice and build up to some more advanced mindfulness techniques. Similar to affirmations and cognitive therapy, mindfulness seeks to retrain your brain in focus, experience, and being present. These will help you better manage the struggles that come with adult ADHD.

Personal Time

As we've discussed, most of the focus issues with ADHD are a result of being easily distracted from a task that is boring or uninteresting. When you have a hobby or task you enjoy, you might not experience the same distractions or lack of focus.

Unfortunately, we are often taught that we can't indulge in what we want to do until after we've done what we need to do. In some cases, that is true. When you have a job with a set schedule, if you choose to sleep in because you want to rather than going to work, you could lose your job and then not have the money to support yourself. There are times when responsibility comes first. However, such an emphasis on responsibility has developed that there is a general lack of encouragement to pursue personal hobbies and passions. Some children are raised being told that they won't have room for hobbies in the "real world."

For someone with ADHD, those hobbies and passions are sometimes the only thing that allows you to relax or recharge. It is the only time you might feel like your brain isn't on fire, or like you aren't distracted by every tiny noise or movement. It can be very therapeutic to have a hobby like this.

The downside is that, if it isn't managed, adults with ADHD will get so immersed in their hobby that they will neglect work, bills, and the responsibilities that do matter.

What it comes down to is balance. By having a hobby or passion, you actually have a chance to exercise time management and organization. A good practice is to give yourself an hour or two (or more if you can spare it) every day to do something for yourself. We don't mean something like take a shower or go for a job; we mean something that is a true hobby or passion of yours. Maybe it is reading science fiction, playing guitar, playing Counter-Strike with some friends, sewing, or baking—something that you don't need to do or feel obligated to do.

This personal time gives you the chance to mentally recharge. If you can do that every day, you won't get so burnt out from stress, insecurities, and the other impactful symptoms and mindsets of ADHD. Give yourself a break every day, and tell yourself it is okay to take a break.

You should go into your personal time with a preconceived time frame. That way, you can set a timer for yourself so you won't forget that there are other things you need to do, or stop paying attention to time. You practice indulging in your hobby, but still go back to responsibility when the time comes.

Part of organization with ADHD is making a clear, well-timed calendar for your daily activities. Include play time on your calendar every day. Set aside an appropriate amount of time that doesn't conflict with other obligations. You should also remind yourself that you don't need to get everything done in one day.

If you have a to-do list with 10 or more chores on it, but you also want to partake in your hobby for a couple hours, still allow yourself the flexibility to reorganize your to-do list so you don't miss out on personal time. Otherwise, you will struggle to focus and complete your chores, then resent responsibility for taking away from your personal time.

So, it becomes about balancing responsibility and obligation with personal time. While your personal time might not directly impact your symptoms, it can help you build skills and also keep your moods up. Not to mention, a lot of hobbies help you develop other skills that can be used to manage your ADHD symptoms. A hobby like knitting, crocheting, or sewing helps you with mindfulness, attention to detail, and usually short-term memory for remembering row and stitch counts.

Playing a musical instrument can be very mindful, relaxing, and improve cognitive function. It can also help you with pattern recognition and improved brain function. Whatever your hobby is, there is a high chance that it lends you some practice with skills that are going to help you handle your ADHD.

Conclusion

Getting a diagnosis of ADHD in your adult life can be very unbalancing, even if it answers a lot of questions for you about yourself, your behavior, and why certain things have been a struggle. Even if you were diagnosed as a child, the symptoms impact you differently as an adult, and it can be hard to make the adjustments on your own.

Understanding and knowledge are going to be your greatest assets in forging ahead and establishing the kind of life that you want. ADHD isn't a life sentence of struggle, medication, and anxiety. Your brain isn't broken or inadequate; you'll just need to get used to how it functions differently than neurotypical people.

Symptoms like hyperactivity, inattention, and impulsivity don't have to rule your life or get in the way of what you want. By now you should have a better understanding of what it means to have ADHD and how those three symptoms impact your life. You should have a greater understanding of why certain aspects of your life haven't come together.

Additionally, you should have plenty of new skills and ideas for starting to organize your life a little better. It'll take time to establish patterns in your routine and thought. The best advice for creating those patterns is just to stick to it. Some days will be harder than others, but over time you will find the best methods for yourself to find the success you are looking for.

From here, start by getting yourself a notebook or journal. It seems like a simple step, but you can use that notebook to begin making your schedule and lists. Start with a pencil so that you can erase and rearrange. It is a good idea to start small, maybe with a daily to-do list. Once you get a better grasp on what your time is like, then you can make schedules and get a calendar for yourself.

Remember that there are a lot of alternative treatment options and self-care options that can help you manage your symptoms. It might be beneficial to start out on a medication, and then once you have a routine and holistic treatment plan in place, ease off the medication so that you don't experience a regression in symptoms. If you do want to alter your medication or treatment plan, confirm that it is a good option for you with your healthcare provider.

Before you begin to rearrange your life, find a hobby that you are passionate about. This is going to be your sanctuary, your recharge activity. Make sure to give yourself some time each day to indulge in that activity.

Most adults with ADHD find that a mix-and-match treatment plan works best, meaning they will combine holistic treatment methods like supplements, massage, and exercise to manage their symptoms. Since this is a lifelong neurological disorder, there is no cure or miracle treatment. It can take some trial and error to put the pieces together for yourself.

If ADHD symptoms have been getting in your way to have the career, lifestyle, and relationships that you want, the good news is, you don't have to let it get in your way anymore. With the tools provided in this book, you have the ability to change the way you approach life, interact with others, and how you handle the symptoms that have been constant roadblocks. Today marks the first day of a future that you have control over.

Hopefully you've had the opportunity to learn more about yourself, and also learn how to help yourself. If you found this information useful, please leave a positive review so other adults with ADHD can get their hands on this book as well. Good luck!

References

ADHD Editorial Board. (20, July 2020). *Adult ADHD: A guide to symptoms, signs, and treatments.* ADDitude. https://www.additudemag.com/adhd-in-adults/

ADHD Editorial Board. (n.d. a). *"I keep my ADHD symptoms under control by…"* ADDitude. https://www.additudemag.com/natural-treatments-for-adhd-in-adults/

ADHD Editorial Board. (n.d. b). *"What it feels like living with undiagnosed ADHD."* ADDitude. https://www.additudemag.com/slideshows/what-undiagnosed-adhd-feels-like/

ADHD EDitorial Board. (n.d. c). *6 natural supplements to manage symptoms.* ADDitude. https://www.additudemag.com/natural-supplements-for-adhd-video/

ADHD Editorial Board. (n.d. d). *ADHD coping strategies you haven't tried.* ADDitude. https://www.additudemag.com/dealing-with-adhd-80-coping-strategies/

ADHD Editorial Board. (n.d. e). *Natural remedies for ADHD: ADD treatment without medication.* ADDitude. https://www.additudemag.com/slideshows/treating-adhd-without-medication/

Bhandari, S. (30, June 2020). *ADHD and stress.* WebMD. https://www.webmd.com/add-adhd/adhd-and-stress

Curtin, M. (30, May 2017). *Neuroscience says listening to this song reduces anxiety by up to 65 percent.* Inc. https://www.inc.com/melanie-curtin/neuroscience-says-listening-to-this-one-song-reduces-anxiety-by-up-to-65-percent.html

Green Lotus. (2011). *Reiki really works: A groundbreaking scientific study.* https://www.uclahealth.org/rehab/workfiles/urban%20zen/research%20articles/reiki_really_works-a_groundbreaking_scientific_study.pdf

Hallowell, E. (01, October 2019). *When ADHD and anxiety collide: Hot to stop paralyzing worry.* ADDitude. https://www.additudemag.com/signs-of-anxiety-in-adults-with-adhd/

Hurley, K. (05, March 2019). *ADHD and relationships.* Psycom.

https://www.psycom.net/adhd-and-relationships/

Itsusync.com. (2020). *Different types of brain waves: Delta, theta, alpha, beta, gamma.* itsuSync. *https://itsusync.com/different-types-of-brain-waves-delta-theta-alpha-beta-gamma-ezp-9*

Koufman, C. (23, January 2020). *Foods to fight iron deficiency.* Academy of nutrition and dietetics. https://www.eatright.org/health/wellness/preventing-illness/iron-deficiency

Low, K. (05, August 2019). *Strategies for living well with ADHD.* verywellmind. https://www.verywellmind.com/living-well-with-adhd-20480

Massage and Myotherapy. (July, 2017). *Massage.* Better health. https://www.betterhealth.vic.gov.au/health/conditionsandtreatments/massage

Mayo Clinic Staff. (n.d. a). *Agoraphobia.* Mayo clinic. https://www.mayoclinic.org/diseases-conditions/agoraphobia/symptoms-causes/syc-20355987

Mayo Clinic Staff. (n.d. b). *Attention-deficit/hyperactivity disorder (ADHD) in children.* Mayo clinic. https://www.mayoclinic.org/diseases-conditions/adhd/symptoms-causes/syc-20350889

Mayo Clinic Staff. (n.d. c). *Meditation: A simple, fast way to reduce stress.* Mayo clinic. https://www.mayoclinic.org/tests-procedures/meditation/in-depth/meditation/art-20045858

Mayo Clinic Staff. (n.d. d). *Mood disorders.* Mayo clinic. https://www.mayoclinic.org/diseases-conditions/mood-disorders/symptoms-causes/syc-20365057

Medline Plus. (02, July 2020). *Vitamin C.* U.S. library of national medicine. https://medlineplus.gov/ency/article/002404.htm

Morin, A. (n.d.). *8 myths about ADHD.* https://www.understood.org/en/learning-thinking-differences/child-learning-disabilities/add-adhd/common-myths-about-adhd

National Institutes of Health. (24, March 2020). *Vitamin D.* U.S. department of health and human services. https://ods.od.nih.gov/factsheets/VitaminD-HealthProfessional/#:~:text=of%20Vitamin%20D-

,Food,%2C%20cheese%2C%20and%20egg%20
yolks.

National Institute of Health. (15, July 2020).
Zinc. U.S. department of health and human
services.
https://ods.od.nih.gov/factsheets/Zinc-
HealthProfessional/#:~:text=Oysters%20conta
in%20more%20zinc%20per,products%20%5B2
%2C11%5D.

Newman, T. (06, September 2017). *Everything
you need to know about reiki.* Medical news today.
https://www.medicalnewstoday.com/articles/3
08772

Newmark, S. (28, February 2020). *10 ADHD
supplements and vitamins for symptom control.*
ADDitude.
https://www.additudemag.com/vitamins-
minerals-adhd-treatment-plan/

Robinson, R., Segal J., & Smith, M. (November 2019).
ADHD in children. Helpguide.
https://www.helpguide.org/articles/add-
adhd/attention-deficit-disorder-adhd-in-
children.htm#:~:text=It's%20normal%20for%
20children%20to,attention%20deficit%20disord
er%20or%20ADD.

Segel, R., & Smith, M. (November 2019 a). *Tips for managing adult ADHD*. Helpguide. https://www.helpguide.org/articles/add-adhd/managing-adult-adhd-attention-deficit-disorder.htm#:~:text=Working%20out%20is%20perhaps%20the,of%20relationships%20and%20feeling%20stable.

Segel, R., & Smith, M. (November 2019 b). *Tips for managing adult ADHD*. Helpguide. https://www.helpguide.org/articles/add-adhd/managing-adult-adhd-attention-deficit-disorder.htm

Shapiro, S. (27, February 2017). *Can you improve adult ADHD without medications?* Psychology today. https://www.psychologytoday.com/us/blog/the-best-strategies-managing-adult-adhd/201702/can-you-improve-adult-adhd-without-medications

WebMD. (n.d.). *Magnesium and your health.* https://www.webmd.com/diet/magnesium-and-your-health##1

Adult attention-deficit/hyperactivity disorder (ADHD) - Symptoms and causes. (n.d.). Mayo Clinic. https://www.mayoclinic.org/diseases-conditions/adult-adhd/symptoms-causes/syc-

20350878#:~:text=In%20adults%2C%20the
%20main%20features

Effective Scheduling: Planning to Make the Best Use of
     Your Time. (2009). Mindtools.com.
     https://www.mindtools.com/pages/article
     /newHTE_07.htm

Melinda. (2019, February 13). ADHD in Adults.
     HelpGuide.org.
     https://www.helpguide.org/articles/add-
     adhd/adhd-attention-deficit-disorder-in-
     adults.htm

Lightning Source UK Ltd.
Milton Keynes UK
UKHW020939120622
404255UK00010B/1462

9 781954 104013